The Middle Path of
Tai Chi

This book shows us how we can walk the Middle Way, the balanced path between the nin (passive) and the nang (active), flowing with the Tao of life.

The Middle Path of

Tai Chi

Peter Newton

New Age Books

ISBN: 978-81-7822-312-4

First Edition: Delhi, **2008**

First published by Findhorn Press 2005

Published by
NEW AGE BOOKS
A-44 Naraina Phase-I
New Delhi-110 028 (INDIA)
Email: nab@vsnl.in
Website: www.newagebooksindia.com

For Sale in Indian Subcontinent

Printed in India
at Shri Jainendra Press
A-45 Naraina Phase-I, New Delhi-110 028

Contents

FIGURE I

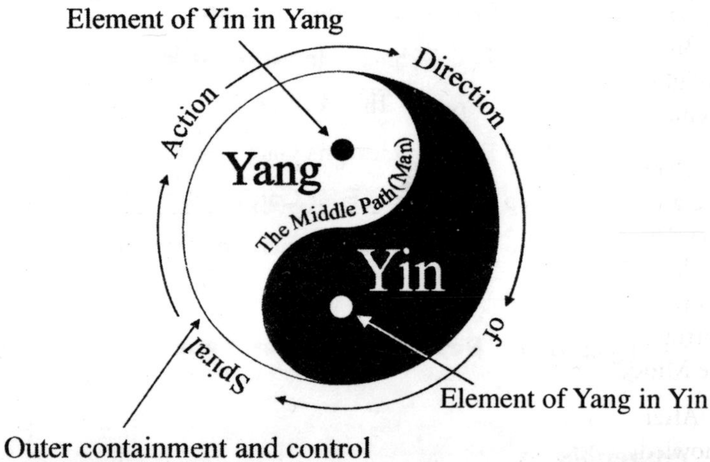
Element of Yin in Yang
Action
Direction
Yang
The Middle Path (Man)
Yin
of
Spiral
Element of Yang in Yin
Outer containment and control

Preface

From a time in Chinese history (circa 4000 B.C.E.) when myth and historic fact are inseparable, an idea was born, which over thousands of years gradually evolved into the highly sophisticated philosophical science called Taoism, symbolised by the popular Yin and Yang symbol (*see fig. 1*). This idea surfaced again in India some 3500 years later, in the mind of Buddha, who regarded it as the pivotal component that guided him to Enlightenment. Now Taoism and Buddhism could boast of a common theme, uniting these two parallel philosophies.

Over the ensuing centuries, the idea became absorbed into Taoist fabric like a colourless dye, discernible only to Taoist academics. In Buddhism, however, it retained its place in the foreground of Buddhist teachings, available to all and fully documented. Although the idea has developed many names, as will become evident, there is only one philosophy that portrays its true meaning most accurately and it is upon this philosophy, the Middle Path of Taoism, that this book is based.

After many years of deliberation, during which I assimilated the knowledge, I gradually began to view the world from a different perspective. Prior to my introduction to the 'enigmatic twins' (Yin and Yang), I am not ashamed to say that I walked in the shadow of ignorance, where negative forces find a safe haven to grow and prosper. Then, at a time in my life when I needed to be guided into the light of awareness, along came the inspirational key to unlock the door to my awakening, in the form of a 94–year–old Chinese Tai Chi master. His appearance in the late 1970s in a television documentary on China brought the physical manifestation of Yin and Yang to my attention for the first time. In addition, there surfaced a hitherto unknown and buried yearning within me to look beyond the human sphere. 'So that's what I've been looking for!' I exclaimed, feeling like a frustrated prospector who had just discovered the mythical pot of gold at the end of the rainbow. At the time I was 75 years his junior and yet

I could not even come close to the amazing balance, grace and athleticism he demonstrated. Now, 25 years later, I am at least on the same waveband that he and the other venerable masters operate on, while they surf the 'Earth-stage' existence.

Since that time, I have had the honour of studying under three highly respected Chinese masters of the Taoist arts, who, like the old Tai Chi master above, have discovered the power, majesty and sanctity of the 'Middle Path'. The 'Power' of the Middle Path is the physical, emotional and spiritual strength it provides; the 'Majesty' is the awe inspiring insights it unfolds and the 'Sanctity' is how it envelops the adept with an impenetrable shield against the unwanted problems life conjures up.

This book is the result of my having spent the last two decades realigning myself to the theories and natural rhythms of Yin and Yang, without realising that I was unconsciously making slow but sustained progress along the Middle Path. This realisation only dawned on me in recent years, when I discovered through research that centuries ago schools of philosophy existed in China and India (Yin and Yang, Middle Path, Middle Way and Half-and-Half) to explore the potential of the original idea. I intend, therefore, to reintroduce and re-interpret the original essence of the idea, which has over the centuries been lost in the misty pages of Taoist history.

Access to this core science has in recent times been limited to a minority of dedicated scholars, simply because, in the main, people 'look but don't see it, and when they see it, they don't recognise it.' The reader of this book will be able to see this hidden science, now that it has been resurrected from relative obscurity (except in Taoist circles), making it accessible to many in a simplified and understandable form.

It is my pleasure to dedicate this book to the tireless efforts of the ancient and latter-day masters of the philosophical arts, who have dedicated their lives (and still do) to sharing the Middle Path message with an ever-inquisitive public in search of a peaceful, prosperous and healthy life. Although I cannot guarantee to materialise this utopian ideal, at least I am confident that here within the pages of this book are the tools to help others to realise their aspirations.

Sifu Peter Newton.

General Introduction

Historically, many of the rich philosophies and practices of the ancient world have, like the human beings who formulated them, flourished then died. Some, however, have been perpetuated while others, like those rediscovered in this book, have been reborn, rising like a phoenix from the ashes of obscurity to benefit new generations. With the dawn of this new age, it is time anew for their ascendance — but for one reason only: their contribution to a greater understanding of the Middle Path and its visual representation the Tai Chi T'u (the Yin and Yang symbol), the core theme of this book.

Sources

The source of the light that illuminates the Middle Path mainly emanates from China; this nation has over the millennia positively abounded with enlightened individuals but is only since the middle of the twentieth century that they have been willing to share their profound science with the western world. This source can be traced as far back as 4000 B.C.E., thereafter evolving in the minds of a string of philosopher sages who gave birth to the philosophy of Taoism.

The Taoists sages are also credited with the invention, discovery and practice of silk weaving; alchemy; cosmology; traditional medicine including acupuncture, moxibustion (the application of cupping and heat treatment over key acupuncture points for healing) and herbalism. In addition, they developed a therapeutic health science comprising Taoist massage, Yogic exercise (Qigong) and Tai Chi Chuan, all of which endure to this day.

The greatest strides in Taoism's evolution were made during the non-warring times, when the population was unshackled from oppression and free to follow the path of spiritual cultivation. This resulted in the birth of the philosophically and spiritually enriched principles documented in the ancient Chinese texts, such as the Nei Ching (*The Yellow Emperor's Classic Book of Internal Medicine*), the I Ching (*The Book of Changes*) and the Tao Te Ching (*The Book of Virtue and the Way*), which despite their antiquity still hold influence over Chinese society today.

In addition, one cannot ignore the undeniable link to Buddha, who through personal and sometimes painful experience created the Buddhist Middle Way School of Thought, which profoundly influenced Chinese philosophers of the same era.

Goal

The goal of this book is to provide, in clear and simple terms, an interpretation and translation of the symbolic root from which all three of the aforementioned classic texts derive their wisdom. This source is represented visually by the Tai Chi T'u, which is more widely known as the Yin and Yang symbol and within which resides the Middle Path (*see fig. 1*).

By nature, people only tend to sustain an interest in a particular subject if it offers personal benefit, whether it enhances their existing knowledge in a particular field of interest, or entertains them by feeding the 'feel-good factor'— like a novel that draws them emotionally into the story. Here, within the pages of this book, resides a story of self-discovery and spiritual enhancement that cannot help but absorb the reader both emotionally and spiritually.

Discovery

Embracing the wisdom of the Middle Path highlights the importance of discovering and applying 'inner awareness', a personalised discipline enabling Earth's mere mortals to see the unknown — something which previously only a privileged few adepts have observed from their dizzying heights. The fountain of knowledge lying at the heart of the Middle Path is so mysteriously profound that wisdom gushes from it like an eternal spring, always 'on tap' to inform, amaze and provide sustenance.

Understanding and assimilating its vibrations and rhythms exposes one to the hidden, or latent, powers which, like sleeping dragons, lie dormant within unless encouraged to venture from their lair. This is human higher spiritual potential (the unlocking of psychic powers) which the Chinese sages named Hun Qi.

Taoist Theme

This book is generally viewed through the medium of Taoism and its popular associated physical and spiritual discipline Tai Chi Chuan.

Taoism is a life long course of study into nature, the universe and all things that dwell therein (the Way, or Tao). It is divorced from politics, rules and regulations; it has no leaders, just followers, who quietly go about their business — content to be in harmony with the Tao. Although the world has changed over the many centuries since the dawn of Taoism, the visual models of its omnipresent force (Yin and Yang) and its philosophical science remain unaltered but adaptable to this modern age.

If it is true when the Chinese sages say 'The Tao is everything and everything is the Tao', then the solution to unravelling its mysteries (in particular the Middle Path) lies within the Tai Chi T'u (Yin and Yang symbol). Add to this the sublime secrets traditionally kept by the sages of old, including the present masters, who are now tending to share this information in a spirit of openness to a much broader audience, and an opaque portal begins to clear.

Advantages and Benefits

What therefore can be derived from this book? From its simplified descriptions and poetic text comes a clarity that brings the hitherto hidden and complex aspects of these arts to a new level of understanding, allowing the reader to benefit from this wisdom. These jewels of the gifted help peel back the outer layers, revealing insights normally inaccessible to the notice of the majority during life's journey. For the uninitiated it would be almost impossible to 'see' what the Chinese masters call the essence or spirit behind Yin and Yang. A full impact of the benefits of acquiring this knowledge will gradually materialise throughout this book, but here suffice it to say in true Taoist tradition that life enveloped with this knowledge is regarded as one that aligns and flows with the current of universal energy (Qi).

A path will now weave its way through what was previously regarded as inaccessible to the majority. The following chapters undertake this quest of explanation and discovery, leading the initiate on a logically structured and achievable route march straight to the Middle Path, and in the process unlocking its secrets.

The Chinese Wisdom Tree

Although the main symbol used in this book is that of the Mystical Path, another could be the structure and growth cycle of an ancient tree, bursting into life as 'a seed of enlightened thought' (the original 'idea') from which sprouted roots, creating a philosophical and cosmological science called Taoism. Having established itself on good and even ground, the sapling science grew to become a broad-bellied tree trunk, encasing this body of divine knowledge. Gradually, wisdom accumulated and expanded like ripples on a pond, seen as the tree's growth rings, which year on year recorded the Tao's rise from the void of non-existence.

Finally, the time came to share these philosophical gems with a wanting world through virtuous individuals who became its far-reaching branches. Here is where their newly founded theories flourished, like beautifully scented blossoms, rich in the fragrance of bloom, with their enlightening messages conveyed to the senses of passers-by on a cool mountain breeze.

This therefore, is the 'Chinese Wisdom Tree', which has as its roots the Tao, as its trunk the body of accumulated knowledge, as its branches the chosen individuals who have achieved enlightenment, and as its blossoms and leaves the manifestation of this profound knowledge in the living world. Just as the tree gradually rose to great heights, so too will those who follow the guidance given in this book, as it builds a pillar of wisdom in easily assimilated stages.

PART ONE

Real people are those who have
Discovered the Real Path.

— PTN

INTRODUCTION TO PART ONE

Truth and Vision

Part One is the most important of the three parts of this book, in that it lays the foundation for the rest to have relevance and meaning. It is comprised of three chapters, which collectively provide the essentials necessary to enable one to see the Way, or the Truth, beyond the visions of mortal beings. 'The Truth' was how the seventh century Chinese followers of the Middle Path School described their doctrines on life. They also referred to them as the True Way — or the True Path — to self-fulfilment and enlightenment.

Another way of explaining this is that people's principles and priorities differ; for instance, someone with limited vision (insight) as opposed to the unblinkered visionary. Both are mortals, yet one can 'see' so much more than the other, who is lost in the fog of ignorance, subconsciously in denial of personal potential and unable to see that there may be room for change. The person of limited vision, according to the theories contained in this book, 'dwells outside of the Middle Path'. The use of the term 'ignorance' is not meant in any way to be derogatory and should, unless otherwise indicated, be viewed in the context of a saintly and honest IT-illiterate person, who is 'ignorant' of the unlawful technical wizardry of a computer-hacking criminal.

What therefore can one expect to achieve by reading Part One? Part One will lead the total novice by the hand through a glossary of the sometimes confusing terminology which accompanies the Taoist arts, to clarify their substance and meaning. It will also enable the reader to develop self-knowledge while becoming aware of all the elements that combine to tell the Middle Path story.

Chapter One
The Path and Its Origins

Before me stands a mountain
That I must surely climb,
The pathway starts where Earth
Meets Sea and Yin and Yang entwine.

– PTN

The Yin and Yang symbol (*see fig. 1*) is nowadays often used by manufacturers and marketing companies as an image that projects 'spiritual coolness' onto a product, in the hope of catching the public's attention. It appears on the likes of: clothing, jewellery, leather goods, general badges, car stickers and even company logos — all designed to help increase sales/turnover. As a result, it is now beginning to imprint itself on the psyche of a curious public, who, although recognising the symbol, are unable to explain what it means or from where it came. To fully comprehend the true meaning of Yin and Yang, it is necessary to examine their source and creator, namely, The Tao.

Taoism – The Source

Taoism is a philosophical science and way of life that evolved from the practices of Taoists, otherwise known as shamans — observers of the cyclic changes of this continually evolving universe — who followed the Tao or 'Way'. How does one describe the 'Way'?

In the true Taoist tradition of presenting the secrets to enlightenment in cryptic verse the sages of old described it thus:

'Those who speak of the Tao do not know it; those who know it do not speak.'

So how does one describe the indescribable? In order to describe the Tao one would need to see it. However, in order to see it, it is necessary to cultivate the ability to open the 'senses' to it, something the average person will never experience in a lifetime, not, that is, without guidance.

Not a word has been spoken,
Not a sound has been made,
Awareness does not even exist.
Yet from somewhere comes something,
We don't understand,
No beginning, no end, no remains.

– PTN

Energy Vibrations

The ancient Taoists concentrated their energies on developing their inner, or latent, senses, to enable them to 'see' the vibrations of the Tao in all things. To them, a rock was as much alive as a tree. And it is just a matter of particle frequency which differentiates between two such unrelated objects. A rock's atomic structure vibrates at a much lower rate than a tree's, and yet they are made up of the same fundamental building blocks, formed from the cosmic dust of the 'Big Bang' or of the 'source' as Taoists preferred to call it. The higher evolved the life form the finer the vibration, with humans at the top of the pecking order.

However, for those who are committed to aligning themselves with the Middle Path, it is important to note: *progression onto and along its shrouded pathway is subject to how high the individual can raise their personal earthly frequency* (*see Tables 4 and 5, Chapter 9*).

Those who are fortunate enough to 'embrace the Tao' (another way of describing Middle Path alignment) will, due to the clarity of mind this brings, realise that their search is over. Most people are constantly searching for answers to their physical and/or emotional problems; they try one thing, lose interest, then try another — never quite achieving the stimulus or result that they seek. It is this blind fixation with 'externalism' (a mind constantly focussed outside of their own presence) which leads them further and further away from the Path. If only they realised that the answer lies within, inscribed on their suppressed spirit-body, for here (when the spirit-body is unladen from earthly constraints and free to soar) is the secret entrance to the Middle Path.

Anything and everything that lives is part of the Tao and when it acts contrary to laws of the Tao, ill health (low frequency) ensues. For humans in particular, this also manifests as a downturn in prosperity and relationships, often leaving them to blame everyone and everything (except themselves) for their misfortunes.

The Te of Taoism

To further appreciate all elements of the Middle Path, the Chinese term Te, requires examining. *Te* means *'Character'*, this being the unique, expressive character of somebody or something, interpreted in its original state through Zen/Taoist thought as

The original nature of the Tao.

It is said that 'Te' *leads* a person to tread his or her own unique way, which is itself the Tao or Path. Te is therefore another way of describing the individual's original form and substance, the 'unsullied spirit' of all living things, and is inextricably linked with the Tao. Te gives someone or something its distinctive shape and quality, and in relation to living beings, it also represents the qualities of mind and feeling or the true character of an individual.

At inception the Qi (life force) in all beings is pure and untainted, free from individual characteristics. It is only when Te gives this singular Qi its character, that the 'formless' becomes 'recognisable form'. This stage is the birth of the individual's Te, which gives each creature its uniqueness in life. Circumstances, however, can alter its inherent character for the better (to complete it — for example when a person realises a natural talent), or for the worse (when for example, someone with a 'God-given talent' in music is restrained from their Te, or gift). From this it can be ascertained that when a person wanders off the Middle Path, they are in fact changing their natural 'Te'.

Notable Taoist Middle Path Sages

The Chinese describe Taoists as Huang Lao, which means students of the respected folklore figures: Huang Ti (circa 2600 B.C.E.), King Wan and his son Tan, the Duke of Chou, (circa 1143 B.C.E.), Lao-tzu (circa 500 B.C.E.) and Chuang Chou (circa 300 B.C.E.). Though there are many more unsung heroes of Taoist history, the six mentioned remain the primary beacons that have shone throughout the darkness.

Huang Ti

This master is said to be the guiding light and instigator of a 3,000 year golden age in China's history, a resplendent period, which produced numerous virtuous philosophers, doctors and scientists (alchemists), who no doubt drew inspiration from this legendary character. In addition, he is called the founder of Chinese civilisation because he was the first real and traceable ruler of the empire. However, in the minds of present-day Chinese adepts, Huang Ti is remembered mainly for being attributed with the authorship of the first fully detailed book on traditional Chinese medicine, the *Nei Ching* (*The Classic Book of Internal Medicine*).

Huang Ti is said to have actually applied the profound medicinal knowledge contained within the *Nei Ching* on himself, and as a result he claimed to have discovered the secret of immortality. The *Nei Ching* still forms the bedrock of modern Chinese medical practices and its author's influence, along with Lao-tzu's and Chuang-Chou's in the forging of Chinese culture, has elevated all three to be China's most respected sons. One thing they all had in common — they intrinsically understood the workings and potential of Yin and Yang, for they talk with the utmost respect of the pair's 'awesome powers' as being 'the best allies and worst enemies.'

According to folklore, Huang Ti lived in the era in Chinese history known as the period of 'Five Emperor Sages' (2852–2579 B.C.E.). The Five Emperor Sages were the enlightened beings, who actively promoted and encouraged the Taoist principles of living totally in harmony with nature (Tao). It was during this period of peace and reflection that spiritual cultivation reached its highest state, as humanity's subtle vibrations were raised to a level where, it was said, communication with the gods became possible.

Refining humanity's vibrations is another way to describe the 'Cultivation of the Way', which is the practice of Taoists who seek to immortalise the Shen (Spirit) by their Yogic arts; these include Tai Chi Chuan and Qigong.

King Wan and Tan, The Duke of Chou

These enlightened ruler sages lived during the end of the Yin (not Yin — the negative energy) and beginning of the Chou dynasties. Very little detail is known about these men of great wisdom and insight, who between them reputedly wrote what is regarded as the 'greatest of the books', known as the *I Ching*, or the *Book of Changes.*

There can be no doubt that this creative father and son were inspired in conceiving the idea of a book of changes by the pioneering work of Fu-Hsi. The I Ching is a book of divination based on Fu-Hsi's Eight Trigrams that were upgraded by King Wan and his son into 64 six-lined hexagrams, said to encompass and embrace the 'Three Powers': Heaven, Earth and Man (*see Chapter 5*). Therefore, all matters, be they negative or positive, affecting the 'Three Powers' are reputedly able to be addressed with the aid of their amazing book. Could this include the age-old question of the meaning of life?

Lao-tzu

Lao-tzu or 'Old Master' (born Li Erh) is probably the best known of the 'three sages', because of the famous *Tao Te Ching* (*The Book of Virtue and the Way*), which must be the most widely read book on Taoism to date. Chinese folklore states that the *Tao Te Ching* was dictated to a border official named Yin-hsi by Lao-tzu, before he left for an unknown destination (rumoured to be somewhere in the western world).

The reverence for his work was plainly evident when, in 1280 C.E., the Mongol ruler of China decreed that all established Taoist literature (Taoist canons) wasto be destroyed — save the works of Lao-tzu. It is obvious his intentions were not achieved totally in this unfortunate ruling, as evidence of the works of the other venerable sages referenced in this book testifies.

Presently, Lao-tzu's immortalised form graces countless thousands of homes, offices and centres of academic learning throughout the world, in the form of statues, carvings and pictures, depicting a cross-legged old sage-like Chinese gentleman, seen riding on the back of a water buffalo.

Master Lao-tzu reputedly lived during mid-Chou dynasty, approximately 500 B.C.E. and is linked through legend to Confucius, who is thought to have met him in his (Lao-tzu's) mountain retreat and told his disciples upon returning that 'He was a plain-spoken man who knew when to speak and when to stop. He also lives in total contentment and harmony with his humble surroundings.' Regarding Lao-tzu's power of mind and depth of knowledge, Confucius commented: 'Such great wisdom, his kind is unique this side of the heavens. He is a phoenix among crows.'[3]

'Chuang Chou' (Chuang-tzu)

This author must be the first ever recorded using a nom de plume, for Chuang Chou chose to write under the name Chuang-tzu. Whether this was to protect himself from any resultant repercussion from authorities he plainly disapproved of is not clear. Chuang Chou, a scholar of the works of Lao-tzu and Confucius, lived during the Warring States period (480–221 B.C.E.) and went on to write the great Taoist classic, entitled simply *Chuang-tzu*. This is a beautifully written collection of stories and monologues which espouses the Taoist wisdom of Lao-tzu and the practical doctrines of Confucius.

Chuang Chou lived during great upheaval and unrest as warlords battled for control of each other's territory, but instead of becoming embroiled in the whirlwind of hatred and violence, he chose to walk the Middle Path of the passive philosopher. His passivity however was tinged with a hard edge; for at a time when it was wise to keep one's head low, he advocated that the oppressed should seek freedom from tyranny.

(Author's Note: Besides these venerable sages, there were many who helped in the development of Taoism through the ages such as: Ko Hung, Chang Po-tuan, Yanf Chu, Wen-tzu, Chou Shou-hsien, Lieh-tzu, Mao Meng, Chang Tao-ling, Ancestor Lu, Liu I-ming, Chou Tun-yi, Wei Po-yang and T'ao Hung-ching. Occasional reference may be made to these revered gentlemen but, in the main, the bulk of the book's material is based on the key ages discussed in this chapter. The essence of the Middle Path lies within the pages of the books referenced in this chapter, of which copies can be obtained (*see Bibliography*).

Tai Chi – The Hidden Parent

Tai Chi Defined

Tai Chi is all of the following: the Unseen Governor, the Central Ridgepole and the Middle Path. It is a hidden force that emanates out from the void, or emptiness, bringing balance to all things in the universe and therefore… life. Its substance permeates throughout and creates the flow patterns of life and death. It gives direction to Yin and Yang, direction that can be seen in the natural courses of rivers, and streams, and the tides that embrace the periphery of the land. The direction of the wind, the sun's and moon's rays, the seasons and the changes that affect life throughout the universe from birth to death — all are examples of Tai Chi at work.

If Tai Chi gives everything form and balance, then it is clearly closely akin to the Tao, in that it overrides all other forces, which may explain why the ancient sages called it 'The Grand Ultimate' and 'Living Breath of the Mysterious Tao'.

These two (Yin and Yang) are considered mysteries;
The mystery of mysteries is the gateway.

– Lao-tzu

If Yin and Yang are 'mysteries', then the 'mystery of mysteries' is how to locate the Middle Path, at the end of which lies the Gateway (*see Chapter 10, The Mysterious Gate*).

Historic Evidence

Arguably, the first documented reference to Tai Chi, the 'Mother of Yin and Yang', appears in the *Nei Ching*, dating from approximately 2697 B.C.E. but formally chronicled circa 1000 B.C.E. It is also referred to in the *I Ching*, accredited to King Wan and his son the Duke of Chou, written approximately in 1143 B.C.E. — during the last days of the Shang and the first part of the Chou Dynasties. Here, the venerable writers refer to the 'Great Extreme' as being the source of the two elementary forms (yin and yang). The Great Extreme is understood to be represented as an *O*, in the figure of a circle.

FIGURE 1

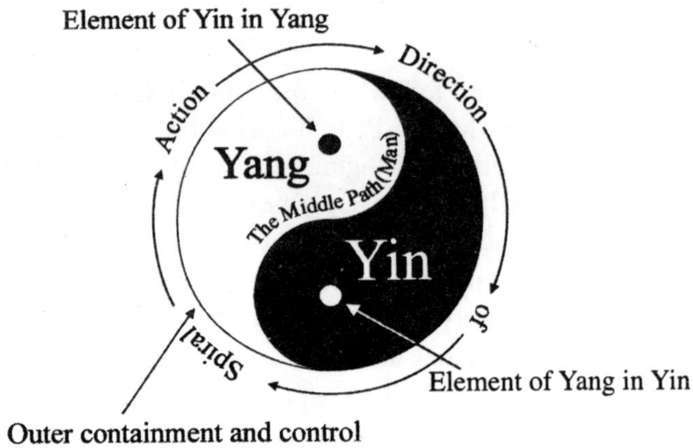

PARENTAL GUIDANCE

Within this circle appear the two, namely, Yin and Yang, but the circle only retains its symmetry when there is harmony between them. These energies are like two young children pulling in opposite directions, abounding with youthful vitality that needs to be kept in check. Just as parents help steer their children through their lives to sustain balance (Mother controls the son and Father controls the daughter, seen as Yin within the Yang and Yang within the Yin respectively), so does Tai Chi its youngsters. If these two powerful energies are bereft of parental control, potentially they run amok losing their shape and mutual harmony.

The moment it stirs a source now exists,
From which matter flows unabated,
Its vibrations reach out into spaces unknown,
It separates and yet it's related.

– PTN

The true meaning of the enigmatic twins tests the boundaries of human imagination and understanding. As intimated in the introduction to this chapter, Yin and Yang symbols, although recognised worldwide, still remain relatively unknown to the vast majority, in respect of their representative meaning. Inquisitive human nature has driven humankind to search the distant horizon for the answer to all life's problems, when in fact it has been right under their noses all the time, in the form of the Tai Chi T'u symbol.

If people were honest with themselves when asked what is it they want out of life, they would all probably agree on the same fundamentals: wisdom, health, wealth and love (both giving and receiving). Well, in this respect, Yin and Yang mean 'the provider and disposer', in that if everyone submitted to and aligned with the heavenly pair's guiding, nature-friendly rhythms, the key to fulfil human aspirations would be provided and the negative, retarding influences would be disposed of. To comprehend the full definition of their meaning, however, will require a comprehensive analysis, which the ensuing chapters provide.

Everywhere you go and everything you do,
Yin and Yang are with you.
They rise with you in the morning
And lie with you when you sleep,
They are the dawn cry of the cockerel
And the descending night's silence.

– PTN

Tai Chi T'u Structure

Structure, in this instance, means an appreciation of the Tai Chi T'u's component parts and an evaluation of their intricacies, to establish the functional actions of each. This is essential to interpret successfully the symbol's potential and thus raise consciousness to new heights.

Tai Chi T'u Symmetry

The first question to address is, why is the Tai Chi T'u circular in form and not square? Answer: Circle = flow and change; Square = stability and stillness. In order for life to flourish, nature (Tao) creates controlled and balanced cyclic change. Therefore, circles and spirals are the inhalation and exhalation of a breathing universe and evidence of this abounds all around; this is highlighted in more detail in Chapter 5.

The square, however, while not being structurally inclined to encourage rotational forces, does offer strength in respect of vertical loading imposed by gravitational force. Perfect examples are seen in the high-rise flats and offices, which endeavour to become humankind's artificial mountains bridging Heaven and Earth. Objects that are square, therefore, remain still, held in place by the unseen hand of gravity.

Tai Chi T'u Components

In order to fully appreciate the extraordinary imprint this symbol has on literally everything in the universe, a brief explanation of its component parts (*see fig. 2*) is necessary:

Figure 2 — Tai Chi T'u Component Parts

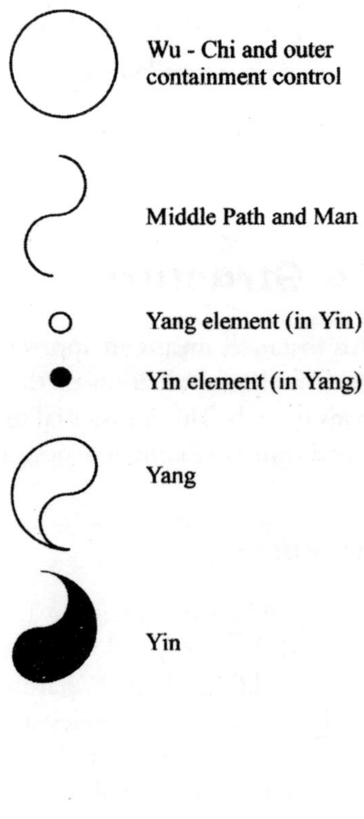

Wu Chi

This literally translates as 'no extremity'; it is a state of total nothingness or emptiness prevailing before the creation of the universe (before the birth of Yin and Yang). The term 'no extremity' refers to the state of being before the controlling influence of Tai Chi appeared (as there were no universal energies to control — there was 'no extremity').

When, in modern scientific terms, the 'Big Bang' occurred, from nothing (which had no extremity) came something (which had, in the form of the mysterious Tai Chi) and consequently for anything to exist in the physical sense there must be 'extremity' (outer containment and control = Tai Chi).

Middle Path and Humankind

The best way to view this enigmatic path is as a sine wave, along which the forces of the universe obtain balance. When placed inside the Wu Chi circle it presents a visual symbol of Tai Chi's handprint on the universe and if the curving line retains its symmetry and balance, then it represents the preferable way for humankind to follow.

Yang Element (in Yin)

This seemingly insignificant white dot that sits centrally in the head of Yin (*see fig. 1*) is the penultimate piece of the jigsaw puzzle that shows Tai Chi's global influence on the cosmos. It is known as the 'Yang within the Yin' and along with the rest of the Tai Chi T'u symbol it acts to stabilise the awesome force of Yin in the universe.

Yin Element (in Yang)

Similarly, this small black dot that appears centrally in the head of Yang (*see fig. 1*) acts in the same way as the white dot in Yin. This is the final piece that completes a full visual representation of the infrastructure of the Tai Chi T'u, which when placed over the rampant, expanding Yang and the all-absorbing emptiness of Yin, acts like a harness to keep both in harmony.

Folklore Origins

Try looking at the base of a giant oak tree and see if it is possible to locate the humble acorn, source of its birth amongst the root system deeply buried under tonnes of soil. This will give some idea of the complexity involved when one undertakes to locate the first physical evidence of Yin and Yang — symbolically speaking. However, in the context of myth and folklore, it is possible to add to its developing historic profile.

Phan-ku The Creator

The mythical Phan-ku was said to be the creator of Heaven and Earth, according to a text of the third century C.E. In Chinese culture before Heaven and Earth were formed there appeared an 'Egg of Chaos' (*see fig. 3*) from the swirling mists of the cosmos (post Big Bang). Within the egg grew the embryo of Phan-ku who had such power that he could harness the prevailing chaotic forces.

Over a period of 18,000 years he grew in stature at a rate of ten feet a day, until finally he burst out of the egg, the lighter parts of which floated upward to form the Heavens (Yang) and the denser sank to form the Earth (Yin). Phan-ku stood tall between (Middle Path) these newly formed kingdoms to hold them in place (Tai Chi or Ridgepole), then, to ensure they endured, he decided to combine his spirit with both.

Figure 3 — 'Phan-ku' and the 'Egg of Chaos'

Fu-Hsi and the Eight Bagua

The Eight Trigrams are also known as the Bagua, meaning the 'Eight Directions' of a compass superimposed over the Tai Chi T'u, each direction having an association with one of the 'Eight Forces': Heaven (*Tien*), Earth (*K'un*), Fire (*Li*), Water (*K'an*), Thunder (*Chen*), Wind (*Sun*), Mountain (*Ken*) and Lake (*Tui*). This obviously predates both the *I Ching* and *Nei Ching* by at least 2000 years and is possibly the earliest reference to the existence of an individual with living knowledge of the workings of the Tai Chi T'u and therefore, Yin and Yang (the *original 'idea'*).

Fu-Hsi, the legendary philosopher king (*see fig. 4*), and the first recorded king in Chinese history, lived during the The Three Sovereigns Period. (This predates Huang Ti, who heralded the following 'Five Emperors' dynasties.) Fu-Hsi is revered as the father of Chinese calligraphy and is therefore the earliest known scholar.

He is also credited with teaching the Chinese nation to cut and carve wood, cook, hunt and compose music, and he and his wife, the mythical Nu-Kua, formed a Yin and Yang partnership. Fu-Hsi is depicted in Chinese paintings with long nails, which were to be adopted by the ensuing scholarly generations as their tribute to his profound wisdom. In figure 4, he is seen sat in a contemplative pose pondering on the unusual markings observed on the turtle's back, from which he is reputed to have conceived the Eight Bagua or Trigrams.

Figure 4 — Fu-Hsi and The Eight Bagua

A Song of the Eight Bagua

Heaven created Earth and Earth created Heaven
Together they forged the wind, thunder and rain.
The Fires within the Earth sculptured the mountains
Upon which the rains fell, pooling in their intimate
Places. This formed lakes and induced the rivers to
Feed the vast oceans. The water engorged Earth grew
Forests enabling a myriad of life forms to prosper.
Man discovered metal, a child of the Earth, and
Applied its strength in war and peace.

– PTN

The Eight Bagua are recognised as evidence of Yin and Yang's bewildering cyclic forces at work in the creation and evolution of the living universe. It is apparent that Yin and Yang were understood by Fu Hsi, for without this knowledge he would never have been able to conceive the Bagua.

Tai Chi Chuan

Tai Chi Chuan ('Grand Ultimate Boxing') is a martial art and health science of integrated motion which aligns the practitioner with the Middle Path, or the centred forces of Yin and Yang. In the western world it is often abbreviated to *Tai Chi*. This can cause considerable confusion, as *Tai Chi* can then either be a martial/health art or a way of describing the grandest, largest thing in the whole universe. Therefore, for the purpose of clarity, whenever the term *Tai Chi* is used on its own in this book, it will mean the grandest and largest. When *Chuan* is placed with it, only the martial/health art will be meant.

Tai Chi Chuan is a vehicle that circulates accumulated Qi ('life-force' or 'air', it also literally translates as 'rice') throughout all the complex energy circulatory systems, *Jinglo,* which permeates the body — much like rivers and streams.

Since its inception in China some 800 years ago, Tai Chi Chuan has carried the elaborate titles of 'Cosmic Dance', 'Absolute Boxing', 'Taoist Warrior Dance', 'Moving Tao Meditation' and 'Taoist Shadow Boxing'; all being relevant descriptions of this enlightening art.

Chang San-Feng

Its creator was Chang San-Feng who, legend states, was a Taoist monk living sometime between the twelfth and fourteenth centuries C.E. Having turned his back on society he took to the mountains in search of enlightenment and came across a remote Shaolin temple. Here he was formally accepted by the monks as a disciple, an action probably hastened by his having had something to offer them also — his knowledge of traditional medicine. They in turn taught him their superior martial arts — acquired through humility, patience, determination and their philosophical wisdom based, in the main, on Buddhism (which, no doubt, will have included elements of Buddha's Middle Way doctrine) and supplemented by Taoism.

Eventually he left and travelled to the famous Wudang Shan ('The Tai Chi Mountain'), in Hubei Province, where he developed the idea for a Middle Path boxing art. This seems to have been made possible by the fact that he now had the combined skills of a martial arts master and traditional medicine practitioner. In short, somewhere high in the recesses of those lofty mountain peaks, he conceived the idea for Tai Chi Chuan, which is a physical (martial) and mental (spiritual) discipline that allows human physiology to align with the health-promoting forces circulating along the Middle Path. As an art, its strength lies in its subtle rejuvenating and enlightening effects, which permeate throughout the mind, body and spirit.

Chang San-Feng then applied this fledgling art to himself and in the process proved its worth by raising his Qi to such heights that he reached the pinnacle of spiritual excellence and thus gained immortality. This feat was recorded in the fourteenth century palace records of Emperor Ying-tsung, who during that period summoned the master sage to share with him the secret of his much sought after inspirational and god-like condition. Having met Master Chang, the emperor honoured him with the title Chen-jen, meaning 'spiritual man who has attained the Tao'. The fact that Chang San-Feng turned up shows that he possibly lived for a period of up to 300 years.

When Master Chang finally took leave of this mortal coil by 'ascending to the heavens on the back of a majestic dragon', he left a legacy of important and enlightening Taoist canons, which included the 'Tai Chi Classics' (to be covered in a later book).

(Author's note: An interesting observation came from my daughter; when I asked her what she thought Tai Chi Chuan was, she remarked, 'It's like exercise, but slower and makes your knees wobble at the bottom.')

Tai Chi T'u

Nowadays, although it is correct to link and associate Tai Chi Chuan with the Tai Chi T'u symbol, it is important not to lose sight of the symbol's original and more profound meaning as seen in figure one, which was flourishing long before Tai Chi Chuan's inception (*sometime between 1200 and 1400 C.E.*).

References to Tai Chi Chuan are numerous in this book for good reason, because it enables the reader to transform the theoretical 'non-tangible' into the 'tangible'. It therefore becomes both translator and 'essence' of the Middle Path, by its gradual manifestation throughout body and mind.

Tai Chi Chuan's Ridgepole

The Ridgepole is a horizontal structure that holds the ridgeline of a tent in an upright position. In order to do this, it relies on the support provided from an upright pole placed directly below it, which in turn derives its power from the Earth, in much the same way the human form must have a ridge (Heaven — Baihui) and a foundation (Earth — Yongchuans) in order to become structurally aligned (*see fig. 7*). Tai Chi Chuan's Ridgepole is therefore the upward lifting force at the crown of the head that creates a good structure and assists the manifestation of power (strength).

In relating the ridgepole to the Tai Chi T'u, it is seen as the uppermost tip of the Middle Path 'S' curve (maximum Yang point) and the pole that provides the structural support is the 'S' curve itself which transfers the load into the Earth at the lowest point (maximum Yin).

(Note: The Yongchuans are acupuncture points located centrally at the base of the ball of the foot through which the kidney meridians breathe and gravity emerges to find its earth. The Baihui point located at the crown of the head is the uppermost point through which the Governor meridian breathes and gravity connects to Heaven. The Governor meridian runs from the groin up the spine and over the head to the face.)

Master Yang Jwing-Ming, one of my own three guiding masters, makes indirect reference to the Middle Path/Ridgepole link with Tai Chi Chuan in his book *Tai Chi Secrets of the Yang Style*, when he states:

> *Those who can comprehend the Tao (Middle Path Way) internally and apply it into external physical actions, with a great level of achievement will reach spiritual enlightenment and sagehood.*

'Comprehending the Tao internally', is classified as Yin (more ethereal than physical), in that it facilitates the following:

- It allows time to take a critical look at one's life through self-assessment.
- It helps one to assimilate the vast theoretical knowledge of Tai Chi Chuan.
- It trains the vision to 'see' the direction of Tai Chi Chuan and align the mind to its flow.
- It trains one to observe the beneficial changes to mind and body.
- It helps one to develop 'internal' training skill (meditation).

Once a positive state of mind has been established through this wisdom, the Yang (physical) actions can commence when this new guiding knowledge is 'applied into external physical actions' that comprise:

- Changes in lifestyle, home, work, and forming negative habits (smoking, drinking, watching too much television, etc.).
- Clearing of all physical obstacles that bar the route to the Middle Path (*See Chapter 5*).
- Commencement of 'external' training (physical rejuvenation through exercise).

- Searching for and locating the Ridgepole by stimulating awareness at the Yongchuan and Baihui points through 'Stillness' and 'Motion'.

Master Yang's next point is his way of saying that rewards only come from regular sustained practice in both 'internal' (Yin) and 'external' (Yang) disciplines. His final statement, 'reaching spiritual enlightenment and sagehood', refers to the by-product of years of careful alignment with the Tao (Tai Chi), which has firmly planted the adept's feet upon the hallowed ground of the Middle Path.

Middle Path/Way: Source and Meaning

The question that must be asked is this: from where does the Tai Chi T'u Middle Path draw its knowledge and inspiration? Is it from the Middle Path School, or from the Buddhist Middle Way? The following analysis should go some way to answer this. However, another even more important question is, what does it mean? An explanation of the fundamental principles of the Middle Path follows to better equip the novice in assimilating the knowledge contained in the ensuing chapters.

The concept and core of the Tai Chi T'u Middle Path clearly lives amongst the many doctrines of the following four schools of thought.

Buddhist Middle Way

Sometime during the fifth century B.C.E., the Buddha, in his search for enlightenment, experimented with his body and mind to see if the answers lay in the dangerous world of extremes (*see 'Excesses/Extremes' in chapter 6 for full account*). By experiencing the destructive force of extremes he found it is in the *centre* where the true safe haven exists. This *centre* he named 'The Middle Way', thereafter referring to it as the 'Great Path' (*Mahayana*), to be followed as the one and only route to enlightenment.

After the death of Buddha in circa 483 B.C.E., his teachings were perpetuated through his disciples who formed into The Middle Doctrine School *Madhyamika*, sometime between 100–200 C.E.

This school of thought was carried to China by Kumarajiva and it was at this stage in its evolution that a fusion of ideals took place, as Buddhist and Taoist thoughts merged into one to form Ch'an Buddhism, which later became Zen Buddhism. Zen came to mean the kind of meditation that is specially aimed at the Tao and Buddha-mind or Buddha-nature.

Chinese Middle Path School

Little documentary evidence exists of the doctrines practised by this school, however it still forms an important part of the jigsaw puzzle when the Middle Path is traced from the past to the present-day. The School of the Middle Path was also known as the *K'ung tsung*, meaning 'The School of Emptiness'. This school was certainly in existence during the lifetime of one of its most revered masters, namely, Chi-tsang (549–623 C.E.). The following is a summary of his and the school's belief system with explanatory notes in parenthesis.

The school proposed the theory of 'double truth' (Yin Way and Yang Way), comprising 'substantial truth' *Yu,* covering all things tangible and real in the physical universe (classed as truth in the common or measurable sense, being the Yang Way) and 'insubstantial truth' defined as *Wu*, covering all things dwelling on the ethereal plane, non-tangible and unreal to the common sense (classed as truth in the higher or immeasurable sense, being the Yin Way).

Unlike many people of that time (and to a certain degree more so nowadays) who only lived in the 'now' and were ignorant of a dual existence (life and afterlife), his school espoused that there existed a 'Middle Truth', which is the real 'now' and only exists because of the simultaneous coexistence between the *Yu* and the *Wu,* the *Yu* being all things in existence and measurable, while *Wu* is having no existence and immeasurable.

'The gift of Truth excels all other gifts.'
– Buddhist Proverb

The original Middle Path School was founded on a coexistence between Buddhist and Taoist disciples who, although they differed marginally in belief (Buddhists follow the teachings of an individual, while Taoists follow the 'Way') agreed on a uniform method to perpetuate the new school's doctrines — or 'Discourse'. Together, they pursued the hidden forces of Tai Chi at work through life's rich tapestry and beyond, into the spiritual realms by means of reasoning through healthy debate, opinion exchange and personal experience through yogic practices.

Written records of their doctrines are few, but those that remain clearly point to the fact that they were observing the forces of Yin and Yang without directly naming them. The most important thing to note about Chi-tsang's Middle Truth is that it clearly highlights the dividing line between Yin and Yang on the Tai Chi T'u, and thus appears to be the first direct reference to the Middle Path.

Philosophy of Half-and-Half

The founding of this school is attributed to K'ung Chi (492–431 B.C.E.), or Tsesse (literary name), grandson of Confucius and author of the book *The Golden Mean,* which espoused a centred life. His philosophy proposes that one can find true fulfilment in the form of a well ordered and balanced life, which lies somewhere between two extremes: that of a Taoist mountain recluse and that of a Confucian activist at the heart of society.

Tsesse no doubt was influenced by his grandfather's teachings, but just as Confucius showed great respect for Lao-tzu, so it appears did his grandson. The Tsesse ideal proposed the establishment of a Middle Pathway through life, which is less extreme and more practical in practice (especially in today's modern society) than the more orthodox Taoist methods. An example of the Tsesse doctrine is cleverly worded in the following extracts from Li Mi-an's 'Half-and-Half Song':

The ideal man lives in half-fame and semi-obscurity.
Half-way in life is man's best state, when slackening
Pace allows him to ease.
And flowers in half-bloom look their prettiest;
As boats at half-sail sail their steadiest,
And horses held at half-slack reins trot best.
Since life's of sweet and bitter compounded,
Who tastes but half is wise and cleverest.[2]

This noticeably differs from precepts of the Taoist purist, who would prefer to live in humbler obscurity, blending into the landscape like a blade of grass in a mountain meadow. Conversely, the Confucian adept is seen at the very heart of society, involved in all its multifaceted intricacies, in particular with the rule of order, scholarly pursuits and the respect of elders and authority.

Yin and Yang School

This is known as the school of knowledge; it emerged from the Fang shih (practitioners of the occult arts) whose 'arts' can be categorised into six classes:

1) Astrology.

2) Almanacs.

3) Five Elements (*Wu Hsing*).

4) Divination (By stalks of the milfoil with the *I Ching* tortoise shell and ox bone fissure reading).

5) Miscellaneous Divinations (Shamanistic fortune-telling).

6) System of Forms (Physiognomy — the reading of facial features and Feng Shui).

Although the roots of Yin and Yang derive from Huang Ti and the subsequent line of emperors (Five Emperors Dynasty), the 'New School' of thought only crystallised when, before his death in 110 B.C.E. (Han dynasty), the scribe Ssu-ma T'an consolidated all the Fang shih arts (Old School) into one volume, which became known as the 'Historical Records'.

The fundamental difference between the 'Old' and 'New' schools is the former were more fortune-tellers than purist Taoists, in that they were happy to seek fame and fortune from their trade, while the latter became synonymous with the Taoist traditions of leading a much humbler way of life in the pursuit of wisdom and enlightenment. The evolution of this sect's beliefs materialised into a manual of 'required behaviour' for emperors and their subjects, creating a workable harmony between ruler, subjects and nature. These were, in fact, the first ever directives on how to find the Middle Path of life.

Ideal Philosophical Life-Span

The following table offers a theoretical appreciation of how the qualities exemplified by the five ideologies mentioned in this book could help establish a Middle Path in a modern society, when spread across the three phases of life:

Table 1. Ideal Philosophical Life-Span

MW/MPS/H&H

Confucian	Y & Y	Taoist
(0–35 years)	(35–50 years)	(50–100 years)
Respectful	Respected	Revered
Growth	Stability	Decline
Aspiring	Established	Retiring
Learning	Learned	Wise
Energetic	Conservative	Leisurely
Radical	Rational	Unassuming
Questioning	Conferring	Reflective

Chapter Two
Maxims for Guidance and Change

Upon the lower slopes of life
In the innocence of youth,
They take our hands and guide
Us to a path sustained by truth.

– PTN

This chapter has three functions to perform, the first being to inspire readers to delve deeper into this book in search of the illusive Middle Path, the second, to prepare them for the horizon — expanding discoveries it contains and the third, to aid them in acquiring the requisite self-discipline needed to follow this course. The chapter title, in fact, contains a deeper message that originates from within one of the core principles of Taoism itself.

The principle that everything must and does change is the driving force behind the whole science of Taoism, including its accompanying symbolism and classic canons. Change, therefore, from the Taoist perspective is evolutionary (and sometimes revolutionary) but always perfectly natural and inevitable, which is how humankind should view it to prosper. Without change, humans plateau, stagnate, decline, then wither as a species, and the same can be said for the universe in general. So, the message here is to embrace change, seek out new challenges and accept and flow with nature's rhythms, for only then can one truly see the wonders left in its wake. In addition, this chapter includes the 'Five Gates of Development' to gauge one's personal experiences against a standard model as the journey unfolds. Finally, a nine-point 'Guidance Checklist" is appended to help pilot the various stages of the voyage.

Middle Path Maxims

Having established the fundamental meaning of Yin and Yang, it is time to clear the mind and open the senses to their existence through an appreciation of the subtle transmissions created by the 'Old Masters' and propagated by the current generation for their selected followers. Here, for consideration, is a selection of Middle Path maxims that were created for those who undertook the voyage into the uncharted waters of self-discovery.

Armed with these 'instructions', they were able to locate and proceed along the winding course of the Middle Path.

'To Know Oneself'

The first advice given to those who wished to venture forth and align with the Tao (Yin and Yang) was to take a retrospective look back at their life's achievements and failures and, in so doing, unveil their own strengths and weaknesses. All aspects of life were reviewed, including: academic studies, work, matters of the heart, home and family, health, and law and order, along with any other negative or positive habitual traits in life generally. This brought their personal Yin and Yang into focus, thereby establishing what was necessary to redress any imbalances that would otherwise have restricted their spiritual growth and enlightenment.

An aggressive, active, pushy, extrovert person would be Yang-loaded, and a passive, lazy, timid, introvert type would be Yin-loaded. After assessing themselves to see which force outweighed the other, they would have applied the results to the creation of a Tai Chi T'u symbol. By commencing with their own personal Tai Chi T'u and understanding its implications, they would have known which areas to target to facilitate balance.

'Silence is Golden'

From the outset it was important not only to be self-critical, but also to establish a frame of mind that became more analytical in discerning the truth from fiction. As the quest got underway two fundamental things needed to be adopted: silence and a thick skin. Regarding the former, it was and still is important to keep a low profile when cultivating the 'self', for without this it could attract unsolicited attention if all and sundry were told of the course of study undertaken. This attention might come in the form of a myriad of self-proclaimed lay teachers who claim to know everything, but in fact know little.

This is where a thick skin comes in; for if the student is approached, they should politely listen to what these would-be teachers have to say and thank them for their advice. Although in the main, most are sincere and occasionally may in fact offer real practical advice, it must be accepted only if it does not in any way deter the student from the planned journey.

Later in the book (*see Part Three*), the 'Silence' referred to here is also equated to 'Stillness', an essential ingredient in achieving the 'golden state of being', which greets the adept at the centre of the Middle Path. In this context, Silence truly is golden and therefore it is wise to start early (now, rather than later) in the cultivation of inner stillness.

'To Be and Not to Be Self-Centred'

In the western mind self-centred only carries one meaning, that which describes people who place their own feelings above considering others. In Middle Path philosophy, this is an undesirable human trait that can blind the perpetrators to the damage this causes to themselves and others (*'not to be'*). There is however another, desirable interpretation of 'self-centred', in which instead of being blighted by greed and cravings, the mind is freed to find long-term peace and contentment when 'centred within' (*'to be'*) and not the external short-termism of self-gratification and self-adoration.

'A Teacher and a Student are One and the Same'

As mentioned in the previous chapter, 'He who speaks of the Tao does not know it and he who knows it does not speak.' Master Yang Jwing Ming, one of my teachers, recently said on this point:

A bottle that is only partially full of water, if shaken
Makes a noise, but the same bottle, when full, is silent.

If the Tai Chi T'u is the Tao, then how can anyone profess to know it? Teachers will therefore always be and remain students. This is why a teacher and student are one.

'Attuning to the Higher Self is not Enough'

It is a well-known fact in Taoist circles that forces evolving at a higher state than mere mortals are at work offering guidance from behind the cosmic veil. They are believed to be the guiding influence on those who seek enlightenment, and yet what these higher energy guides are unable to do is to provide the drive and self-discipline necessary for an individual to progress. Many are those who without the will to sustain the effort needed fall by the wayside and no doubt their frustration in failing to reach their full potential is shared by their spiritual helpers.

What we lack is discipline,
A discipline fed by Shen,
To be the best, better than all
The rest, you must try again
And again and again.

– PTN

This *Shen* referred to means 'spirit', and must be sought and nurtured to find the Middle Path. It is a known fact that many people who waste valuable time and effort in the search for self-fulfilment, through their intrinsic weakness, walk in the shadow of ignorance. Time after time they sample hobbies and pastimes such as painting, carpentry, yoga, languages, photography, Judo, origami, karate, keep fit, and Tai Chi Chuan, to name but a few. But before they even get under the surface layers, their minds begin to wander as the usual uncontrollable urge redirects them to pastures new.

To benefit from anything and in order to make a valued judgement, time must be allowed to absorb sufficient knowledge on the chosen subject. Only then can a true picture form as to whether it is the fated vocation or preordained path that they, in all innocence, hoped it would be. It is by allowing this 'time to experience' that they will truly find fulfilment in life.

As the physical vibrations of the enlightenment seeker heighten, the ethereal world of the spirits finds it easier to access the seeker's subconscious mind. Therefore, expect a spirit *sifu* to make itself known in the form of inexplicable insights, dreams and unusual coincidences. *Sifu*, in general, means teacher, and is a term used by the Chinese for anyone on Earth or in the spirit world who has wisdom to share. In this instance, it is the spirit guide who is referred to, a non-physical being who is well equipped to steer its Earth-bound ward along the road to personal enlightenment.

In the Chinese martial arts and Taoist arts community, it is generally accepted that spirit teachers are assigned students in order to continue their research and the development of their art.

It is certainly an impressive thought and an honour to find in keeping with the principles of Yin and Yang that both physical (*Yang*) and ethereal (*Yin*) teachers offer support. And what of setbacks? Instead of allowing the emotions to rise, analyse their meaning, for more often than not they are there to teach a lesson after which one can continue with renewed strength. It is by opening a channel to these spirit guides that they can, to a limited degree, help create the conditions for advancement.

'Patience is a Virtue'

Poorly motivated people tend to become enveloped by their own frustrations and consequently wander off into the barren lands of apathy, never to be seen again. However, for those who endeavour and win the first internal battle in the war that rages within (or, in some, just simmers), a weight is lifted from their baggage-laden shoulders:

Look to the heart for the answers, through patient eyes.

– PTN

Frustration surfaces more readily in those who expect too much, either from themselves or others. How many lost souls have trod the boards of the philosophical arts over the years, with great expectations of the teacher's abilities? They look with their sad, inquisitive eyes hoping that the teacher can solve all of their problems. One can almost hear their minds leaking thoughts such as: 'I wonder if he is the Messiah?' and 'Oh... he's normal! That's a disappointment.' They almost expect with a wave of a hand to find the panacea for all their aches, pains and worries. However, when the penny drops and they realise health and wellbeing come only to those who work for it, they put a line through the attempt and drift aimlessly away.

The answer does not lie in the alchemic contents of a pill; on the contrary, it lies in the naturally occurring alchemic content of mind and body. Transformation of both can only be achieved through a more disciplined approach towards finding and strengthening the spirit.

If the frustration barrier is negotiated then beneficial changes ensue, as the toes are tentatively dipped into the ocean of Tai Chi T'u knowledge. After only a few short months, the fog that once clouded the senses begins to clear and, as a result, it is possible for the first time to see the same strains of negativity that blight mind and body… in others.

Down endless paths I wander
In my search for me,
But each one leads to nothing
And nothing is all I see.

– PTN

'Contemplate on the Oral Transmissions'

Many gems of guidance are released to air from the lips of modern-day teachers, who are not all necessarily eastern but their message is uniform and helps humankind to stay on the 'straight and narrow' (another way to describe the Middle Path). The majority of the potential receivers of this guidance choose to focus on what they perceive as more important: monetary gain, fame, power and materialism. They are both blind and deaf to the real source of happiness and riches — spiritual contentment. Within lies the real jewels, that when found radiate their power outwardly to provide a healthy and loving environment for life (and beyond).

In other words, these gems that are released to air by a venerable teacher tend to fly over the head of those who are not ready to interpret the message. However, if one scribbles down an apparently unclear oral transmission, one can be assured at a later date it will make sense and thereby convey the recipient onward and upward with its knowledge. For example, this drop of wisdom that stems from the interface between Tai Chi Chuan theory and Taoist philosophy:

To be empty means being full, and to be full means being empty.

Most of those present at the time looked blankly at each other while trying to fathom his meaning. In time, however, its interpretation became clear: When the mind is empty of inordinate desires, and the muscles, tendons and ligaments of tension, only then can the body be full (of Qi). Conversely, if the body remains full of tension and unbalanced thoughts or desires, then it will consequently be empty (of Qi).

For those who endeavour to put these words into practice it will make a tremendous difference to posture, breathing and stress levels generally. The same principle of recording should be applied to the insights or messages that can appear in the form of dreams, images during meditation or flashes of inspiration, all of which may be sent to keep the trail to the Middle Path open.

'Look Back, but Never Go Back'

As the Middle Path draws closer, expect to look and feel different; attitudes and emotions that previously ruled alter too, leaving a clearer mind to see one's own mistakes and those of others who still walk outside of the Tao. The following short story of a Middle Path master's encounter with a highway robber offers some hope to those who have 'stepped off the Path':

Healing Encounter

Between the hidden folds on the upper slopes of Shen Shan (Spirit Mountain) and a peasant village nestled against its forest-coated hemline, there winds a path. And along this single track appears an elderly but fresh-faced and light-footed man the villagers call the Jade Master. His expression is serene; his spirits perpetually elevated; for as he progresses through the dense woodland, he sustains no fear of man or beast.

Though most men know not of the truth he has discovered, the beasts of the forest positively rejoice in his presence leaving a chorus of birdsong and animal chatter in his wake. He is on his way to the annual festival of harvest blessing, where he, in the capacity of spiritual advisor and on behalf of the simple village folk, offers thanks to the Five Elements for providing the favourable conditions to grow their healthy and abundant crops.

About a mile outside of the village, the forest trail merges with a wide road that joins the village to the more densely populated coastline, and it is along this tree-lined highway there patiently sits a rogue, waiting for his next victim. Secreted behind a boulder, close to the edge of the track, he springs an ambush on the old master, thinking him to be a wealthy trader from the lowlands. The robber's intentions were to smite the innocent traveller down dead, with one swing of his broadsword. However, the master had already anticipated the attack and with lightning reflexes, he grabs the attacker's wrist, disarming him. The surprised robber offers resistance and, therefore, with an effortless wave of his hand, the master sends his totally perplexed assailant flying back through the air some 20 feet.

Dazed, winded and sitting on the seat of his pants in the middle of the dusty road, the robber gazes up at the face of the master who, much to his surprise, now stands beside him, bestowing the sword.

Before he can say anything, the master speaks:

'What you endeavour to take is without reward, that only serves to fire the coals of bitterness and pain. This, however, is your sword, which I return to you freely along with one other gift that can only be bestowed and not forcibly taken.'

The robber, now standing, receives the sword, which he promptly slides back into its scabbard. Now he is able to look directly into the master's eyes, which have such crystal clarity he feels their gaze bore deep into his sorry soul. The master continues: 'You have been wronged by ignorance, born from the shadows of hate and greed. And yet, you choose to walk deeper into the same blackness that blights your soul, instead of seeking the Pathway into the light, where love, peace and harmony await. If you must resort to theft, then when your inner demons are asleep, steal their thunder, remove their belongings and cast them out onto the cold streets. Only then will you become wealthy beyond your wildest dreams.'

With tears in his eyes, the robber turns and walks solemnly away, repentant for all his evil deeds and yet elated for being released from the grip of his past. After a few strides, he stops and turns to thank the old sage for his gift, but the sage is gone, it is as if he has melted away into the forest — like an early morning mist.

Those who go back, dropping out for whatever reason, will soon notice the difference as the accumulated homeostasis dissipates, leaving coordination, balance, flexibility (assuming Tai Chi Chuan option), emotional stability and psychic potential to slide, as the refined vibrations step-down from their previously highly evolved state. More often than not, most are able to return, but those who turn their backs on the Tao find they are in fact turning their backs on themselves.

The secret of the Middle Path is its simplicity,
Look deeply and see blackness.
Therefore, to 'see' you must not look,
Instead, just find the centre and openly receive.
– PTN

In summary, one should *never go back* to the old way of walking (or in some cases staggering) through life, now that a clearer and healthier path lies ahead, but that does not mean one should never *look back*.

To know the outcome, look to the root.
Study the past, to know the future.
– Chinese Proverb

'Use Knowledge to Feed the Wisdom'

It is a different world nowadays compared to the much slower paced lifestyles the sages would have encountered. Then the less densely populated landmass was so great it could comfortably support and secrete those who dropped out of society to live a hermit life of solitude and contemplation.

Therefore, the wise journey-man who seeks balance in the modern world should study the ancient philosophical texts, learn basic human anatomy, digest and contemplate on the awesome Tai Chi T'u and even keep an eye open for the odd magazine article, television documentary or radio programme that may be on a related subject. Filling the memory archives with useful and appropriate knowledge gives the 'Wisdom Mind' a pool to draw from when the Middle Path draws closer. This data, which is held in the subconscious mind, will subsequently come to the fore, to safely guide its host through the difficult stages. Above all, it is necessary to open the eyes and observe life in all its myriad forms, to manifest the conditions favourable for enlightenment.

The Five Gates of Development

The following 'Five Gates', record the typical life-changing experiences generated by the combined disciplines of Tai Chi Chuan and Middle Path philosophy. From day one, to year ten and beyond, physiological and spiritual changes take place which are rarely documented, especially in a time-line format. Here, for the first time, is a brief but comprehensive written account of human evolution when the programme is followed with balanced dedication.

Gate One — Self-Realisation (First Month)

Awareness raised of tension and stress levels results in stiffness in joints and limbs, compounded by age and or lack of exercise; of a lack of balance and coordination irrespective of age — even in children. Poor respiratory function caused by general irregularities in posture restricting Qi circulation.

Note! At this stage, frustration is felt at the realisation of one's limitations, especially when compared to established practitioners.

Gate Two — Basic Changes (After Six Months)

Tension and stress levels begin to noticeably drop as the message and training sinks in. Joints and limbs become more fluid (wooden arms and legs develop silk-like properties). Balance and coordination improve, increasing circulation generally, thus diminishing the potential for falls, especially in the elderly. The breath begins to sink deeper into the lungs aided by the releasing of stiff and tense muscles. Posture improves and an awareness of Qi (Life-force energy) develops.

Note! Dividends are paid for the first time due to sustained effort.

Gate Three — Inner Awareness (After Two Years)

Qi begins its journey to the extremity of the limbs. Changes in posture free the breath. Balance and coordination become refined. The *Yi* ('Mind') and *Shen* ('Spirit') are stirred. Joints and limbs are now loose and free flowing. Skin tone and condition improve and Qi gathers at the Dan Tien ('Main Lower Energy Centre').

Note! Having experienced the above beneficial changes, the appetite grows for further development.

Gate Four — Point of No Return (After Five years).

The *Qi* ('the breath') propels the limbs. The *Shen* ('Spirit') negotiates its way throughout the meridians or *Jinglo* ('Qi pathways'). Stress becomes bridled and its symptoms dissipate from body and mind. Less sleep is needed. Common ailments such as colds and flu pass by. Actions become instinctive. Eyesight becomes clearer. Eyes become clearer. Height marginally increases, due to posture improvements. Yin and Yang energies flow without restriction and thus harmonise. Hearing becomes sharper and all the joints in the body become buoyant with Qi.

Note! Continuation beyond this gate will expose the threshold of the true Taoist experience.

Gate Five — The Journey Begins (After Ten Years).

Human frailty is no longer of concern. The powers and wonderment of Mother Nature (*Tao*) are seen for the first time. A sixth sense appears from within, as both 'Sky Eye' and 'Heaven's Gate' awaken. Healing powers arrive. *Ching* (sexual energy) is absorbed through regulating this activity. The Dan Tien becomes the centre of the universe and others feel its presence.

Note! Beyond this gate lies the universe, where all barriers dissolve and the Shen is free to explore the cosmos.

Middle Path Guidance Checklist

1) Establish the theoretical meaning of Tai Chi, from a universal perspective.

2) Seek out the children of Tai Chi and observe their manifestations in the largest and minutest detail.

3) Build on personal strengths, while eliminating 'Qi-sapping' weaknesses.

4) Be prepared to rationalise beliefs, ideologies and lifestyle patterns that restrict personal growth.

5) Through meditation and openness, seek out the direction and rhythms of Tai Chi on Earth, so that alignment to its subtle streams is made possible.

6) Pay attention to others, to see the healing and destructive forces of Yin and Yang at work, for this will help locate the route to the Middle Path.

7) Find the Middle Path of the home and workplace, in respect of surroundings and personal relationships.

8) Study and become familiar with the basic workings of human physiology and anatomy. For by understanding how something works, maintenance and improvement become possible.

9) Listen to the inner Tao; it advises when it is time to sleep, wake, rest, work, eat, drink, make love and go to the toilet. It also offers guidance when important decisions are to be made. Those who ignore these natural impulses will fall on stony ground.

Chapter Three
Yin and Yang Relativity

You call it Yin and I call it Yang
For we all have a different view,
To some it is black to others it's white,
But we're right to believe as we do.

– PTN

In locating the Middle Path it is important to understand how the principle of relativity works between the 'inseparable two'. Labelling *this* as Yin or *that* as Yang can be subject to variation, depending on the object being assessed and the personal view of the assessor.

General Examples of Relativity

Compared to a dog, a cat is Yin, but next to a mouse it becomes Yang. During a recession redundancies are rife, poverty increases, relationships are stressed and dramatic lifestyle changes take effect — all Yin by nature, and yet through it all the seeds of the opposite (Yang) are present in the form of receivers who see a boom in their business, and civil services (social services, benefits agency, etc.) who are gainfully employed processing the unfortunate by-products of recession — the unemployed.

'What appears as a Yin, may in fact be a Yang,
The whole matter is highly conjectural.
Although cast in stone it transforms like a cloud,
From a positive to ineffectual.

– PTN

According to the Middle Path School, any object (something or somebody) is transformed in perception (Yin = Wu or Yang = Yu) by the mind (*Yi*). For example: a decision made to demolish the garden shed makes the shed both *Yu* (tangible, Real Truth) and *Wu* (non-tangible, Unreal Truth) simultaneously. This is because as soon as the decision is made (in the mind) to demolish the shed it ceases to exist as it was previously perceived; therefore it transforms to *Wu*. Although at this stage it still remains intact as a functional shed and therefore as *Yu*.

This is Yin and Yang transmutation where one can be instantly changed into its opposite, triggered merely by a thought impulse. In the mind, the focus of the thought's attention changes its character within a split-second from Yin to Yang or vice versa, as is seen through the shed analogy as those who still use the shed while it awaits its demolition see it as it is...a shed. But to the individual who decided to remove it, it has become Yin and therefore not the shed it was.

This can also be applied to buying a new car and the sense of pride its newness (Yang) brings, which swiftly changes the moment the decision is made to sell it and buy another, now it is the old, unwanted has-been (Yin). But for the person who buys it as new, it becomes once again a 'wanted' joy (Yang). Plainly the Middle Path School's 'Double Truth' is another way of packaging relativity.

Relativity in the Martial and Health Arts

In relating the Tai Chi T'u to Tai Chi Chuan from a martial art and health art perspective, considerable confusion exists in the field when discerning the Yin and Yang of their general application. Therefore, this section will compare and correctly label their relevant intricacies.

Martial Breathing

The in-breath = Yin and out-breath = Yang. This relates to the power breathing method called *Heng and Ha*, where *Heng* is the inner sound made as air is drawn in through the nose and condensed at the Real Dan Tien (*see fig. 7*). This is used to pull and uproot an opponent, or for coiling prior to releasing a punch, chop, push, or kick.

The sound of *Ha* (projected outward through the mouth) is the release of the energy that has been drawn inward, like an arrow on the string of a bow by the action of Heng. The lower abdomen is now relaxed and expands outwards as the breath leaves the body. This 'condensing breathing' draws the Qi into the marrow of the bones on the Heng and outward into the muscles and skin on the Ha (*see Chapter 6, Breathing Essentials*), an action that carries considerable benefits to health (if delivered with a slow, smooth and even breath), besides the devastating power it releases from the body in self-defence.

Health Breathing

The in-breath = Yang and out-breath = Yin. This is the opposite of martial breathing because in matters of health the in-breath is looked upon as being positive, refreshing and the bringer of life and energy, therefore Yang. While the out-breath is classed as negative, as it releases the body's spent fuel (carbons) which by nature are toxic, and therefore Yin (*see Chapter 6, Breathing Essentials*).

Therapy and Martial Joint Locking

The art of joint locking in Chinese martial arts is called *Chin Na* which translates as 'grasp and control'. It involves the manipulation of joints into positions that are intended to cause great discomfort to the recipient. In addition it is common to apply force into pressure points, or 'cavities', which can cause excruciating pain.

Joint locking is therefore Yang (powerful and dominant) in its application and Yin (painful and submissive) in its result. However, relative to health the same techniques that would normally debilitate can, if applied gently, be positively therapeutic; for example, soft manipulation and flexing of the wrist, elbow or shoulder joints increases the ROM (range of movement) and strengthens tendons and ligaments. Also, mild pressure on acupuncture cavities (acupressure) stimulates Qi through the linked meridian and associated organs. In this case, the application is Yin (gentle) and the outcome is Yang (positively helpful). Under-usage of joints and muscles creates stagnation and weakness. Over-usage creates excessive wear and tear damage. The Middle Path method of manipulation and cavity stimulation is positively therapeutic in keeping meridians flowing and joints and muscles open, flexible and strong.

Earth (Kun)

Another example of Yin and Yang relativity is how Mother Earth can be perceived. In relation to the Tai Chi T'u in figure 1, Earth should be placed exactly halfway down the Middle Path line at the centre of the circle because, according to the Five Element theory, Earth is the Middle Path controller of all the other elements:

> Earth = Yin, in that life is spawned from its womb as an expectant mother; Yang, in that it is a solid ball of matter in the vacuum of space (Yin). It is Yin, in comparison to the Sun (Yang); Yang, compared to the moon, which is a dead satellite (Yin). It is Yin, in that 70 % of the Earth's surface is covered with water; therefore Yin dominates.

Thus relativity of human perception is unique, as can be gleaned from the following story:

The Incorruptible Spirit

High above the palatial peaks of a sacred mountain, there flies a solitary white crane soaring on the warmed air currents that rise off vast, fertile plains, laid as a patchwork quilt at the mountain's gently sloping feet. Suddenly, something catches the crane's penetrating vision; so inquisitive by nature, it sweeps down to investigate. The object of the crane's attention is a solitary sage perched in contemplative meditation on a flat rocky prominence boasting a grandstand view over a glistening waterfall. After circling the old man a while, the crane feels confident enough to land only a few feet away.

'Master, why do you sit here all alone with naught but a bubbling mass of water for company?' asks the crane.

The master chuckles quietly to himself and replies. 'Because I choose to, and as for being alone, the river is one of many friends I have all about me.'

The crane thinks for a moment before continuing his line of questioning.

'Master, have you therefore no friends from where you come?'

'Yes, of course, I have!' rebounds the reply. 'Many, but their visions and values differ from mine.'

'Then Master, how did they become your friends if they walk another path?'

'Because through their eyes I am as they and they are as me.' This response silences the crane for a few seconds, then he retorts.

'Why is it then that you can live amongst men and yet be so at home here in this distant valley?'

The Master, now standing with his whole body bathed in radiant glory by the sun's new dawn, replies in a tone as clear as the water below:

'Here I am myself and when I walk in the world of man, the Great Tao bestows upon me a gift. It is the gift of change and adaptation while still retaining my true character. Whereas you, my dear friend, you have no need for pretence, a crane you are and a crane you will always be.'

When a roving eye is cast across the myriad of things that reside within the universe it is wise to keep relativity in mind.

From all things negative, comes a positive reaction.
From all things positive, comes a negative reaction.
Therefore, Yin is Yang and Yang is Yin.

– PTN

The next chapter looks at how humans and all other life on the planet are influenced by the power of Tai Chi in their daily lives, but to close this chapter, here are the general rules for Yin and Yang.

If it is hard, brittle, sharp, expanding, hot, luminous,
Moving forward, rising, explosive, centrifugal,
Aggressive, loud, male, acidic, uncompromising,
Domineering, old, healthy, good, enlightening and positive,
THEN IT IS YANG!

If it is soft, flexible, blunt, contracting, cold, dark,
Moving backward, sinking, implosive, centripetal,

Timid, quiet, female, alkaline, compromising,
Dominated, young, unhealthy, bad, ignorant and negative,

THEN IT IS YIN!

(*Depending on which way you look at it*)

– PTN

PART TWO

Those who mutually embrace Heaven and
Earth find the path within,
While those who embrace only one will forever be
lost unto themselves.

– PTN

INTRODUCTION TO PART TWO

Through the Eyes of the Tao

Part One having laid a general foundation of understanding, Part Two unfolds a deeper appreciation of the keys to finding a personal Middle Path through life. Within the pages of this middle section lies the main body, a torso of wisdom that enables readers to see themselves, and life in all its forms, 'through the eyes of the Tao'. This involves superimposing a translucent Tai Chi T'u over the next three chapters, which explain how all Earth's creatures must rely on, and relate to, the subtle interface between Heaven and Earth to survive.

The information herein will take the new wisdom hunter to a higher level of clarity and help to explain why everything prior to this stage was clouded by life's trials and tribulations.

Chapter Four
The Median-Line Through Life

It weaves a path through everything
That dwells beneath the skies,
An unseen hand embracing all
No matter what shape or size.

– PTN

Yin and Yang Perceptions

Mr Yin and Mr Yang

To illustrate the extremes that emerge when people move off the Middle Path, the following dialogue introduces Mr Yang and Mr Yin, two unfortunate characters who are trapped in their self-induced stagnating states. They are the 'slippery-slopers' who slide into oblivion as the seeds of their own destruction are sown within their transfixed personalities.

Mr Yang — Mr Yang is a centrifugal repulsive person who tends to dominate all and sundry; he has no patience, no rational thought, cannot sustain relationships, is a poor listener, suffers from high blood pressure and angina and is not a man to be crossed. He wears very loud, colourful clothing, as if to amplify his nature, which also describes his choice of music, which he insists the rest of the world should listen to. He eats, drinks and smokes heavily and 'couldn't give a damn' what anyone else thinks!

The excesses of yin or yang prevalent within
Mankind are as noticeable as a gentle cascading
Waterfall or a solid rock face on the landscape

— PTN

Mr Yin — Mr Yin, on the other hand, is a centripetal 'black hole' personality who saps the life out of all who venture too near his event horizon. He is a loner, a quiet-natured but bitter person, who keeps his frustrations bottled up inside causing untold damage to his health. Others of a more Yang disposition tend to dominate him and his patience is legendary to the point of being irritating. He will listen to complete drivel until the cows come home, he tends to be a deep thinker, cannot sustain relationships — as partners get frustrated with his lethargy — suffers from low blood pressure and has developed a weakness in the kidneys.

A typical conversation between the two would go something like this:

Mr Yang: 'Hi, Mr Yin, how the hell are you?' (Crushes Mr Yin's hand in vice-like grip.)

Mr Yin: 'Well, I'm not too good really.' Silence.

Mr Yang: Yes, me too. And how's the wife?' (Turns away out of the wind to light another cigarette.)

Mr Yin: 'She died last week.' Deathly silence.

Mr Yang: 'That's great, and how about those kids?' (Opens diary and flicks frantically through the pages.)

Mr Yin: 'We never had any children on account of my, err... problem.' .... Embarrassing silence.

Mr Yang: 'That's good to hear. How is work?' (Looking at someone across the road.)

Mr Yin: 'I was sacked last month for taking too many sick days.' Sickly silence.

Mr Yang: No response. 'Well, it's been great speaking to you, but I've got to go and kick some ass.' (Slaps Mr Yin on his back, triggering a coughing fit.)

Mr Yin thinks to himself, when he has regained control of his breathing, 'What a nice man.'

Yin and Yang Power At Work

These powerful forces can steer a course through people's working lives both positively and negatively. From very early childhood, some people can develop enviable and natural attributes in: golf, football, art, music, etc… and, if circumstances allow, are fortunate to pursue careers they enjoy. Though some may fulfil their dreams and aspirations in this way, the majority end up in jobs totally unsuited to their personality and natural talents, leading to adversity in health and prosperity. An example would be an outgoing Yang personality who is entrenched in a position that has no interface with colleagues or customers. This is a volcanic-like scenario, where stress levels rise proportionate to the frustration felt from the failure of the company to utilise the employee's strengths. Everyone has strengths and weaknesses that should, like water, find their own level (Middle Path). In this way they align with the Tao and do not cut across the grain, which leads to negativity and conflict.

The Middle Path way creates calm, centred efficiency
As opposed to rushed uncentred inefficiency.

– PTN

The Job Interview

Here is a situation where an 'off-centred' employer with a Yang disposition is welcoming a new and nervous employee of Yin disposition to his pack:

The aggressively driven employer greets the nervously twitching novice with a handshake strong enough to subliminally implant the impression of 'I could crush you like a grape!' As the blood slowly seeps back into the flesh of the now disfigured hand, he leads the quarry into his 'den', which the lip-biting greenhorn visualises as a lion's lair of a place; probably carpeted wall to wall with the bleached bones of staff who did not conform! His office is in fact characteristically draped and carpeted in red, to camouflage the bloodstains of previously disciplined unfortunates. There, on a malnourished milking stool of a chair, he sits the pale-faced victim down. This is in striking contrast to his high-backed settee-like throne, which looks at home behind a desk boasting the same landmass as Norway.

Slapping his heavy hand down on the desktop with a force that measured .5 on the Richter scale, he barks 'Right my lad, I run a tight ship here, so don't rock the boat and we'll get on. Are there any questions?' From a previously unknown void, high in the back of the visibly shaking young man's throat, there resonates a reply that is comparable to a gerbil on helium: 'Could you tell me where the toilets are?'

This type of leadership is called 'motivation through intimidation', which only has a short shelf-life, as nobody thrives or gives loyalty in a threatening or hostile environment.

On the other hand, a weak emotional leader who is likely to be an innovative and creative thinker, but who leads from the rear, impresses many but inspires none.

A Middle-Path centred leader inspires the workforce by leading quietly from the front with a clear, rational mind. Such a leader seeks neither glory nor fame and is able to overcome challenges, when they arrive, by recognizing and using the Yin and Yang strengths of the support team.

Success

To those who crave fame and riches, the drive for success can become intoxicating. Forced success is only one-sided; it is unfulfilling and short-lived, while 'natural gravitational successes' based on a sensible interpretation of the Taoist Middle Path are meaningful and sustainable. For example, those who force their way to the top are notorious for leaving a trail of debris in their wake, upsetting work colleagues, friends and family in their blinkered drive for success. When they finally get there, the strain of it all will have damaged their health and relationships, leaving them little time to enjoy rewards, which are shared with no one.

True sustainable success comes from putting one's aspirations into perspective, by removing the desire for excessive wealth and fame. And by setting achievable (not self-gratifying or impossible) targets; this keeps one's feet firmly on the Middle Path, and brings the support of work colleagues, family and friends.

Other Middle Path Work Related Maxims

'Expect nothing and gain much' — While the mind is fixed on concern for what rewards can be gleaned in the future for self-gratification, the now becomes less clear and is overlooked. This creates problems which hinder sustained growth that would otherwise generate sensible rewards for all involved in the enterprise.

'Push and meet resistance' — This maxim applies to all aspects of human life including work. It is all about finding the middle ground when interfacing with fellow humans, irrespective of the topic being discussed. Nobody likes to be pushed into making decisions; therefore, at all times compromise and harmony must be sought to avoid confrontation.

'Plan for difficulty when things are easy' — Although this again applies to all facets of life, it originally became known as the maxim of Sun-tzu, who scribed the famous Art of War. Here, he was saying that the time to keep your guard up is when you feel safe from attack, during times of peace. This is because he knew the 'guaranteed to evolve' cycles of Yin and Yang would create conflict once again from calm. Therefore, when at work, and business is buoyant, plan ahead, make contingencies for the worst, then look forward to long-term survival.

'Don't strive for perfection' — The great Tai Chi master Chu King Hung, once said about human's view of perfection: 'When people look at a statue they tend to admire the one with the nose knocked off and arms missing, calling it a work of art. However, show them one which is perfectly intact and they don't give it a second glance.' While the universe is subject to the laws of Yin and Yang, there will never be such a condition as 'perfect'.

Ying and Yang Careers

Finally, as a point of interest, here are some of the careers which Yin or Yang people tend naturally to gravitate towards:

Yang	Yin
Entrepreneurs	Receivers
Salespersons	Accountants
Mid-wives	Funeral Directors
Cultivators	Florists
Police	Prison Officers
Paramedics	Doctors and Nurses
Builders	Demolition Contractors
Chefs	Waiters
Manual Workers	Clerical
Army	Navy
SalvationArmy	Priesthood
Political Leaders	Spin Doctors

This list is just a general categorisation, and, as discussed in Chapter 3, any one of the careers on it could switch columns depending on the chosen angle of consideration.

Yin and Yang in Personal Relations

Love and Hate

This is where the powers of Yin and Yang manifestly express themselves, as most people will already appreciate:

No matter where you travel,
No matter what you do,
Love breaks down all barriers
Like a knife that cuts right through.

– PTN

What is love? Why is it so powerful? They say it conquers all, and this is correct, providing it is kept in perspective and in balance. Alternately, non-existent love destroys a balanced relationship:

A heart that is distant creates a wilderness around it.

– Chinese Proverb

On the other hand, groomed, harnessed love is the most powerful and positive force in the universe:

Love's subtlety is Yin and blessing is Yang,
In conflict it causes much pain.
When lovers depart their sadness is real,
Reunited, they have much to gain.

Where love has no home, there flourishes Yin,
If created, the greatest of Yangs.
Lasting more than one lifetime it goes on and on,
But can change like the shifting of sands.

PTN

At the two ends of the spectrum are love (Yang) and hate (Yin); no other emotions act upon the human psyche like these two. Both have, in their uniquely intricate ways, caused mayhem throughout history, by driving the human spirit to do unspeakable things. It would therefore be wise to avoid their extremes. For those who love in excess can fall into obsession and ruin what would otherwise be a fruitful harmonious relationship. (The object of their intense affection usually feels suffocation and flees.)

On the other hand, to dislike someone or something is quite natural, but when dislike is allowed to mutate into hatred, it can not only destroy the object of this venomous onslaught, but can also ruin the life of the aggressor.

To conclude, a perfect illustration of how the Middle Path controlled forces of Yin and Yang work in nature to perpetuate life is seen in the subtle oestrogen-enriched power of Yin, emanating from the female, which both attracts and intoxicates the male, and conversely, the testosterone-soaked vibrations which emanate from the male, which are alluring to the female. When both of these hormonal emanations are harmonised through mutual attraction, equilibrium transpires, creating a healthy and sustainable Middle Path between the couple.

Confrontation

The truly awesome power of Yin is evident in the following scenario:

A man threatened to punch his friend, while they were out for a drive in his new car. The absent-minded friend had opened the passenger-side car door while the car was still moving and bent it around a concrete post, displeasing the car owner greatly. Slamming on the brakes, the furious driver jumped out, ran round to the passenger side of the car and ordered his friend to get out, so that he could punish him with an act of wanton violence (excessive Yang). Through the red mist, he watch his friend calmly stepping out onto the pavement, showing no sign of fear, or any physical aggression in return to his threats.

Now standing face-to-face and looking the aggressive car-owner squarely in the eyes, the friend quietly assured him in a relaxed but firm, unwavering voice, 'If you lay a finger on me, I'll kill you (Yang within the Yin).' To say he took the wind out of the driver's sails is an understatement; his calm and centred reaction had totally transformed an uncontrollable rage into a rationally thinking, passive state of mind (Middle Path).

The passenger's attitude was a perfect example of the subtle power of Yin to cancel out and transform excessive Yang. The Yin that the passenger portrayed was the perfectly curved symmetric Yin symbol, complete with the Yang 'fish eye' (*see fig. 1*) opposite element at its core, which represented the inner strength the passenger showed through his calm Yin exterior. Although, it is important to note it was only because he had his feet firmly planted on the Middle Path that the harnessed power was able to manifest in the first place.

The lesson to be learned here is that when faced with imminent aggression, the body language and voice pattern response will determine whether a physical attack is forthcoming or just threatened. When an assailant is intent on inflicting physical harm on another person, their threats will materialise if shown excessive Yin or excessive Yang in response. Excessive Yin subliminally invites the attacker in and feeds the rage, so that the aggressor feels safe in the knowledge that all defences are down, confirming total dominance. On the other hand, an excessive Yang response is like pouring petrol on the flames, which equates to the Taoist view that

Two Yangs (or two Yins) are a mutually destructive partnership.
— Taoist Precept

What does one do with a situation where someone has flipped into a suicidal and hysterical state (excessive Yin)? Roaring at them and beating them (excessive Yang) will only make matters worse. It is the controlled and firm Yang response (centred from the Middle Path) that brings order to chaos. A perfect example of this in action is when the hysterical person is told to stop in a strong but unthreatening voice, which works most times. However, when all else has failed, a sudden slap across the face (Yang but not too excessive) will bring a Yin excess back to a controllable, balanced Yin state, where sense and reason can be applied. If any doubts remain as to the power of these two forces that control peoples lives, just ask a parent 'What are the affects on you when your new baby cries?' A baby's crying is the most powerful expression of Yin power the human mind is subjected to.

Chapter Five
At the Heart of Feng Shui

A Tiger and a Dragon will lead
Us through a door, behind which
Lies all answers to the questions
Posed before.

– PTN

This chapter offers practical advice on creating a cooperative environment for Tai Chi (and therefore the Middle Path) to flourish, whether it is in the home or at work, and will look at the link between Tai Chi and Feng Shui. The first thing to establish is the definition of *Feng Shui,* which translates literally as 'Wind and Water', two elements the ancient Chinese believed to be fundamentals of nature, whose interaction between Heaven and Earth work in harmony to sustain or, if out of balance, destroy life. Feng Shui stems back some 5000 years and is a form of *geomorphology* (a branch of geology which examines the formation and structure of the features on the surface of the Earth).

Although only wind and water are represented in its name, Feng Shui in fact encompasses all the five elements, or *Wu Hsing*: Water, Fire, Metal, Wood and Earth. Its science proposes that here on the Earth are places where these five forces, guided by the unseen hand of Tai Chi's Middle Path, work in harmony to create life, and conversely, where their unbalanced interactions become positively destructive.

The aim of Feng Shui is to guide people to live in harmony with their surroundings — especially with the location and layout of any habitations where humans spend time, be it at home, at work, socially, or for recuperation (hospitals and clinics). Problems arise when the natural flow of Qi is interrupted or distorted, which creates negative Qi affecting health and prosperity. When Qi becomes imbalanced, the Chinese say that the Yin and Yang are not in accord. Yin and Yang represent both negative and positive energies respectively, which if combined into two mutually supportive halves create true healthy Qi. The Taoist sages of old were said to be able to *see* the vibrations of this true Qi, through powers acquired in their quest to find the Great Way, or Middle Path. This chapter will help the reader to 'see the light' and to understand how the great Taoist sages, who aligned their subtle frequencies with the surrounding forces of nature, became the living embodiment of Feng Shui.

The Three Powers of Feng Shui (San Cai)

The Chinese believe that chaos follows when the three most important powers (*Qi*) in the universe lose harmony, these being: Heaven (*Tien Qi*), Earth (*Di Qi*) and Man (*Ren Qi*).

And of all the lessons to be learned, this is the most important before embarking on a personal quest to find the Middle Path. The concept of the Three Powers clearly places mankind alongside (in status) and between (as a bridge, *see Phan Ku*) Heaven and Earth, as elected communicators and custodians of both. If Heaven is Yang and Earth is Yin, and man connects both, humankind must therefore be the Middle Path of this tripartite union.

A wide world lies half-way twixt heaven and earth

– Lin Mi-an [3]

To the Taoist, man must align with the Qi of Earth and of Heaven to find the trail to enlightenment (this also applies to health and living a long, fruitful harmonious life on Earth).

Feng Shui – Tai Chi Link

The forces of Mother Nature lie at the heart of the ancient science of Feng Shui, which maps and profiles her positive and negative effects on all living things (especially humans). These forces are catalogued and placed into the camps of Yin or Yang respectively, represented in Feng Shui symbolism as a White Tiger for Yin and a Green Dragon for Yang. The cycle of birth and death is prevalent within the subtle and dynamic forces of nature and if kept in balance and harmony, a healthy environment is created for life to flourish.

Without the hidden influence of the Tao, which manifests itself through Tai Chi — the governor, the controller, the Middle Path —, both Dragon and Tiger would run amok and ultimately destroy all life. Therefore:

A gentle breeze that caresses your cheek,
A gale that knocks you off your feet,
The ripples on a passive lake,
The tidal wave with death-wrapped wake.
All answer to what made them be,
The inexplicable and mysterious Tai Chi.

– PTN

Spirals

Many years ago, scientists proclaimed the universe is being subjected to a spiral action which is driving and shaping the galaxies and solar systems, the imprint of which can be seen in the galactic spiral clusters that pepper the universe (*see Fig. 5*). Where else does this occur? The short answer is… 'Everywhere!'

Figure 5 — Galaxy Spiral

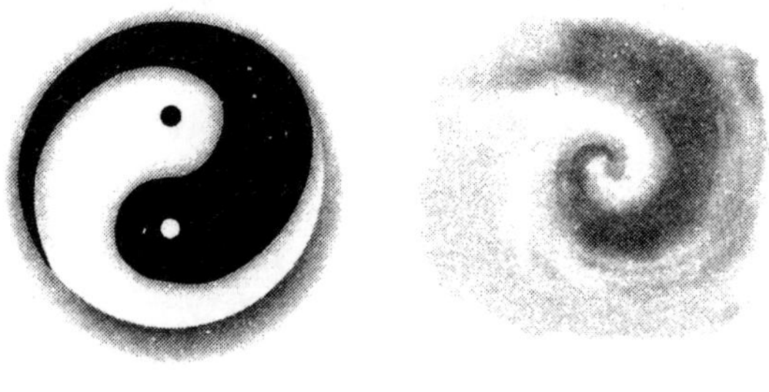

In the cord that feeds your phone,
In your voice when you ring home.
In your ear that hears the sound,
In the rope that ties things down.
In the ringlets on your head,
In the springs inside your bed.
In your vessels and meridians too,
Which blood and Qi flow through.

In the thumbprint on your hand,
In the cornfields on the land.
In the corkscrew shaped pig's tail,
In the shell of a sea snail.
In the winds of a hurricane,
In the ebb and flow of pain.
In the umbilical cord at birth
And the ley lines through the Earth.

In the screw that holds things down,
In the ring road around the town.
In the ivy on the wall,
In the spinning of a ball.
In the whirlpool in the sea,
In the roots that feed a tree,
The numbers are too great,
Where spirals congregate.

– PTN

This universal vortex is the result of Tai Chi's influence on the forces of Yin and Yang, and the central generator is the three-dimensional core of the Tai Chi T'u, called the Ridgepole, or Middle Path. Spiral energy also featured in the belief systems of ancient peoples such as the Celts, who depicted the Earth's ley lines and spirit gateways in the form of spirals, seen on the many stone monuments spread throughout the Celtic world.

The art of Tai Chi Chuan aligns itself with this universal spiralling energy (Qi) and in so doing improves the functional rhythms of body and mind (*see 'Jade Step Four', Chapter 8*).

Feng Shui of Training

This is an important aspect to consider for Middle Path students, because the environment chosen to practise in can be detrimental or positive in its effects on health and development.

Place of Training

Both indoor and outdoor locations are subject to positive and negative forces; it is therefore important to locate and sometimes create their healthy zones, or Middle Paths.

Indoors: This is likely to be in one of two places, the home or the training hall. In the home, it is important to select the appropriate room for a physical workout and meditation respectively, and I would suggest considering two separate locations if one does not meet the criteria. And just what are these criteria? The following list may help:

- Illuminate with natural light and avoid fluorescent lighting which has a negative frequency.
- Ensure adequate ventilation supplied by fresh air.
- Avoid draughts that attack the body like arrows.
- Ensure sufficient background heat to feel comfortable.
- Avoid rooms with negative outlook (for example overlooking a factory).

- Avoid rooms with unpleasant odours.
- Avoid heavily patterned walls and strong colours.
- Avoid distractions of television, radio, neighbours or family.

In the training hall, the basic criterion remains the same, which is if possible to make it environmentally comfortable. However, very few are in the fortunate position of owning their own hall, and, therefore, are unlikely to be able to dictate its furnishings and layout.

Outdoors: Here, it is especially important to choose the correct Feng Shui location, due to the obvious effects weather has on the human body. Before going into the details of outdoor Feng Shui, it is important first to consider the following list of do's and don'ts of training:

- Practise regularly in cycles; sporadic training is a waste of time.
- Do not eat a heavy meal or drink copious amounts of fluids for at least one hour before, or after, any physical or internal training.
- Do not train while under the influence of drugs or alcohol.
- If taking medication, or suffering or recovering from an acute illness, seek the approval of a doctor.
- Wear loose fitting clothing.
- Wear clothing to suit the season.
- Do not train when it is: too cold, hot (in direct midday summer sunlight), humid, wet, damp, windy or draughty.
- Do not train if exhausted or emotionally charged.
- If afflicted by colds or flu, adopt a gentle regime.
- Do warm ups, sustain comfortable frequency, and then cool down.
- Never train to exhaustion.

Remember, the general maxim for all training considerations is:

Those who cut across the Tao
And ignore its mighty streams,
Will fall into a state of flux
And shatter all their dreams.

– PTN

This means, listen to the body and respect its needs, the Tao has given humans this inner sense to help them through life, and those who lose contact with their inner voice, do so at their peril. There will be times the message is a resounding *no* to any physical exertions, as the 'wisdom mind' (inner conscience) knows its limitations. (Don't be like those middle-aged fitness fanatics who try to relive their youth by competing with younger, sprightlier contestants on the squash court. Their excessive exertions too often result in being wheeled out hastily on a paramedic's stretcher, en route to the local cardiac unit.)

If practising outside and the weather conditions feel uncomfortable, either move to another location or practise inside. At all times, seek the approval of the Feng Shui energy, which is there to please, if consulted.

Health Ramifications

The following is a layman's guide to the dangers of off-centred negative Qi in the home or place of work. Firstly, let's establish the definition of *negative Qi*, which is a term for the detrimental effects of extremes and insufficiencies of Yin and Yang Qi:

Yin Qi	Yang Qi
Noxious substances	Sharp penetrating drafts
Creeping damp	Light invasion
Insects and vermin	Severe water penetration
Toxic seepage	Seasonal extremes
Clutter	Aggressive decor
Dirt and grime	Obsessive cleanliness
Inappropriate usage	Parties
Inadequate ventilation	Over ventilation

There are many more that could be added to the list, but at least these will put negative Qi into perspective. Now, from a Qi point of view, the list will be reviewed in more detail.

Yin Qi

Noxious Substances — This nuisance penetrates the senses in a subtle but obviously irritating way; its source may be a local chemical plant, a farmer's muck-spreading, a gas main leak, fumes from a gas fire, a nearby motorway or petrol station. But worst of all is the household chemical cocktail in the form of bleaches, washing powders, washing up liquids, hair shampoos, air fresheners, insect sprays, surface cleaners, perfumes, deodorants, hair sprays and protective coatings on clothes, carpets and furnishings.

Creeping Damp — The most Yin element Water is a perfect example of Yin power, in that it can overcome the most solid of obstacles and wear them down through erosion or rot. A home that has been breached takes on a Yin perspective, from the dampness, which pervades its structural materials, fabrics and atmosphere. For the residents this causes an increase in conditions such as bronchitis, asthma and arthritis. In addition, the home is likely to experience an increase in insect infestation, as the damp conditions are favourable to woodlice and cockroaches.

Insects and Vermin — Death-watch beetles, ants, woodworm, bees, wasps, hornets, flies, rats, mice and spiders all covertly enter the home or workplace, causing untold damage to the building and its occupant's health.

Toxic Seepage — The inside of the home or office is Yin by nature, creating a small vacuum that draws in air and therefore gases from the outside. An example of a subtle Yin invisible danger is radon gas, which permeates through the porous concrete floor into the rooms and if inhaled increases the potential for cancer to strike.

Clutter — Qi flows in much the same way as water in a hosepipe: if there is a kink in the line it restricts the flow considerably. Clutter in a building acts in the same way diverting, weakening and even blocking the healthy Qi flowing through the rooms and hallways. Remember the maxim: 'Running water stays fresh, pooled water becomes stagnant'.

Dirt and Grime — Lack of cleanliness can cause friction between the occupants and provides a breeding ground for germs.

Inappropriate Usage — A home should be a home and an office should be an office; neither should impinge on the other. When the two meet, work output decreases. as does the time set aside for relaxation and recuperation.

Inadequate Ventilation — Here again, a breeding ground for germs; each room should have a regular cyclic air change to keep the air quality fresh. Stagnation of ventilation creates an imbalance resulting in elevated levels of pollutants and stale air.

Yang Qi

Sharp, Penetrating Draughts — This nuisance is described by Feng Shui specialists as 'arrows that pierce the body', and acts in much the same way inflicting damage. Draughts derive from poorly fitted doors and windows, which funnel the usually cooler air into narrow spiral streams. This materialises in the occupants in the form of stiff necks, backs, shoulders and often chills to the kidneys.

Light Invasion — This can be either direct or indirect, though both are equally dangerous to the recipient if the frequency is unfriendly. Direct (without reflection) may be from a neighbour's glaring security light, which keeps bursting into life every time a fieldmouse breaks wind in a pasture two miles away. Other sources could include the sun, especially in the morning or evening, as it sits low in the sky, and the headlights of passing vehicles or even badly located street lamps. Indirect (with reflection) are usually from the same sources as direct, but can be magnified in damage potential by the object they reflect off. For example, a broad beam of light particles may be focussed into a virtual laser when reflected off a picture frame, a highly polished surface or glazed ornaments. A common symptom of this problem is regular recurring headaches or migraines.

Severe Water Penetration — This appears as flood and storm damage that punches its way into the living space causing havoc, as ceilings collapse and carpets, furnishings, appliances and clothing are ruined. The stress this causes is the main concern to health.

Seasonal — Each season has its negatives; for example: Summer is a nightmare to hay fever sufferers and can make life difficult due to water shortages. Autumn can be a time of heavy rains and winds, not to mention the nuisance of leaves blocking gutters and causing accidents on roads, rail and underfoot. Winter disrupts home and work with heavy snowfalls, frost damage to pipes and numerous accidents due to ice. Spring is a time of unexpected flooding due to pipes thawing and high spring tides.

Aggressive Decor — Bright red, orange and yellow wall, ceiling and floor finishes, enhanced by sharply outlined patterns, attack the senses making it impossible to create an atmosphere for relaxation. Someone who lives or works in this kind of environment would tend to be extrovert, loud, brash and short-tempered, and ultimately likely to suffer from hypertension.

Obsessive Cleanliness — This also includes obsessive tidiness and when both are combined they are as conducive to relaxation as an operating theatre. No germs will survive in a place like this; however, neither will too many humans. (From a health perspective the home should neither be too clean nor too dirty. Half way between the two encourages healthy bacterial resistance to flourish in the body.)

Parties — These leave a wake of destruction, especially in the home and a lingering atmosphere of negativity that can last for weeks. The home loses its recuperative properties if abused this way, eventually exhausting its occupants.

Over Ventilation — This is usually perpetrated by the 'obsessive cleaner', who has over many years become accustomed to living and working in a wind tunnel. But as for the rest of the occupants, they can empathise with the struggles of Scott of the Antarctic.

Noise Pollution — Excessive noise invading the home or place of work can disturb the natural rhythms of Qi in body and mind. Unwanted noise invades the senses causing a loss of concentration and a feeling of unease that can lead to sleep deprivation.

Relative Feng Shui

Feng Shui is also subject to the relevancies of Yin and Yang described in Chapter Three. For example, Qi that is acquired indoors is Yin and that acquired outdoors is Yang. Since the early dawn of humankind, nature has encouraged people to return to their caves or dens for rejuvenation of the body's cells, which implies indoors is purely for rest. If outdoor activity is for work, exercise and play, then according to traditional Chinese medicine, both Yin (indoor) and Yang (outdoor) must be cyclically balanced to promote good health. In short, a similar amount of time should be spent in both environments.

The role of Feng Shui in this is important in that, to fully rest, the home must have a Middle Path, along which Qi will flow unrestricted. Additionally, in order to benefit from the treasures of outdoors, an equivalent 'exterior path' must be located. This is exactly what the ancient Taoist sages did when they retreated to the mountains. They took an exorbitant amount of time and patience in searching for the perfect Feng Shui location for their shelter and surrounds. For they knew how important these two factors would be in their quest for immortality and how they would be held back if either were out of balance.

Through a profound knowledge of Feng Shui, it is possible to 'see' the Tao's streams and, therefore, become wise to the environment in its positive or negative sense.

Chapter Six

A Path to Health and Fitness

The Tao has natural rhythms
Which are there for all to see,
But some ignore her guidance
So she bends them like a tree.

– PTN

Welcome to Chapter Six, the most important. It is a chapter that particularly targets those unfortunates living in the shadows of excess Yin or excess Yang, who are the most in need to be guided onto the Middle Path of health.

As the body moves closer to the Middle Path, what can only be described as 'transparency' materialises, a condition where the physical, 'cellular body' is brought closer to the realms of the ethereal 'Qi body'. If this physical and spiritual higher frequency state is the goal of Middle Path teachings, how then does one describe the conditions prevailing prior to achieving transmutation of the cells and Qi? The short answer is as 'opaque'— visibly, audibly and generally 'opaque' from a health and spiritual viewpoint.

The visible signs are: a general dullness to the skin, eyes and hair; and an excessive weakness or strength in the voice, reflecting the imbalance of Yin or Yang respectively. Opaqueness of body and spirit can also be detected by the unattractive body odours released through the skin, breath and body waste. All, when transformed, either emit no odour or give off pleasurable fragrances known as 'Fragrance Qigong', a known esoteric phenomenon associated with high level adepts who walk in the blossoming gardens arrayed along the Middle Path Way. Spiritually non-visible cloudiness manifests as emotional imbalance, caused by loss of centre and focus; this also is the origin of the visible problems already mentioned, which are the outward expression of inner opaqueness.

Middle Path Rejuvenation

People differ greatly in their general level of health. In this, as in other things, each individual is unique. The following chart (Fig. 6) may be used to plot one's progress back to health and enlightenment.

Figure 6
Middle Path Rejuvenation Time Line Chart

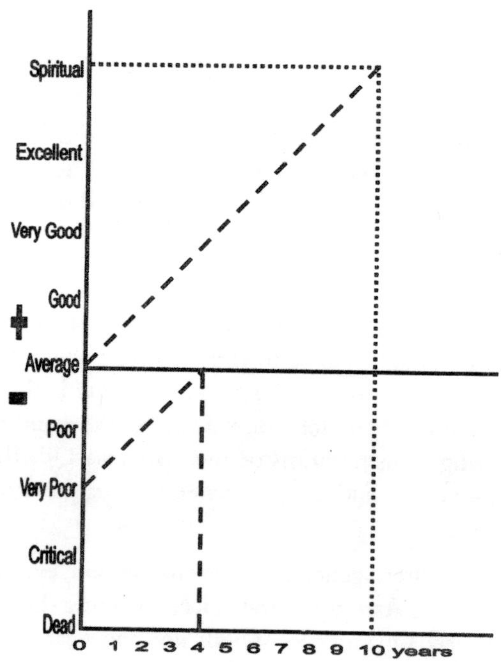

The example shown is for a person below the average health line, someone with very poor health, who has commenced the Middle Path journey not just to find the way back to average health, but also to explore the spiritual path. As can be seen, to recover average health will take such a person 4 years; and if it takes a person with average health 10 years to acquire the spiritual frequency, then it will take an individual with very poor health: 4 + 10 = 14 years to accomplish the same.

The Extremes/Excesses

According to the *Concise Oxford Dictionary,* extreme is: 'Outermost, farthest away from the centre, situated at either end.' This, as Buddha found to his cost is a place where humans should not dwell too long. The health ramifications of extremes or excesses that are under examination here are best analysed by overlaying this definition on the face of the Tai Chi T'u. In figure 1, the 'centre' is located halfway up the Middle Path line and, therefore, the 'outermost' of both Yin and Yang extremes are 'situated at either end' respectively.

The higher the climb, the farther the fall.

– Chinese Proverb

These positions are known as 'Maximum Yin' and 'Maximum Yang' and are extreme poles of great symbolic importance. Extremes in traditional Chinese medicine are categorised as 'deficiencies', or 'excesses'. Both are classed as extreme conditions of Yin or Yang and never is this more apparent than in the extreme experiences of Buddha.

Buddha's Middle Way Experience

An excellent way to drive home the dangers of wandering down the uncharted paths of extremes is to briefly tell of Buddha's painful lesson learnt when he chose to test his limits. For reasons best known to himself, Buddha decided to seek the answer to enlightenment by aggressively subduing his human passions. First, he explored his respiratory system by progressively holding his breath for longer and longer periods. This according to historical records gave him painful headaches and no spiritual uplift. He then turned to an extreme diet for the answer: He reduced his food intake to miniscule proportions, just a spoonful of bean soup a day. This caused his hair to fall out and he lost his physical strength and weight.

From this self-imposed excessive regime came the reality of the Middle Way in the form of a vision of the god Indra. In the vision, Indra was playing a three-stringed harp. The first string was too loose and could produce no sound. The third string was too tight and snapped when plucked. It was only the correctly tuned middle string that could produce the desired sound. At that point Buddha knew he must abandon his extreme experiments and find a more balanced approach, if he was to find true enlightenment.

This is the voice of the Middle Path, directing from within, guiding those who tread the hazardous trail of extremes back into the centre and safety.

Excess Yin

This is indicative of an empty vessel desperately in need of filling and in terms of the human body it presents itself as:

- Blood — low pressure, circulation poor, chemistry of cell count imbalanced.

- Qi — Yin in ascendance, Yang descending.

- Bodily Functions — bladder releases that are colourless and frequent. Bowel movements that are loose and frequent.

- Skin — pale and cold to touch.

- Voice — weak, lacking power.

- Spirit — low, lethargic with a feeling of not being able to cope.

- Pulse — weak, slow and deep.

- Eyes — dull, glazed, with white of eyes visible below iris.

- Tongue — pale with white coating.

- Hair — lank and dull.

He spent his time killing time,
Until time finally killed him.
– Traditional Irish Proverb

Excess Yang

This is indicative of a full vessel overflowing and in need of partial emptying. It presents itself as:

- Blood — high pressure, with poor circulation, but outwardly projected to the surface, manifesting as flushed redness of the skin. (This condition can also indicate imbalance in endocrine system.

- Qi — Yang ascending, Yin descending.

- Bodily Functions — bladder releases that are dark orange, cloudy and infrequent. Bowel movements that are solid and infrequent.

- Skin — red with eruptions and hot to touch.

- Voice — coarse and loud.

- Spirit — agitated, over-confident to the point of being irritating.

- Pulse — strong, fast and shallow.

- Eyes — red, with white of eyes visible above iris.

- Tongue — red coated with yellow fur.

- Hair — dry, brittle and animated.

Natural Causes of Disease

By *natural causes* is meant 'extreme exposure to natural elemental conditions prevalent on the planet', and by *disease*, 'when the *ease* (fluidity of movement in all physiological and emotional actions) is disturbed'. In keeping with the natural laws of Yin and Yang, Table 2 summarises the excesses that must be avoided to remain on course along the Middle Path of longevity.

Table 2 Excesses: Health Connection

Emotion	Climate	Organ
Joy	Heat	Heart
Anger	Wind	Liver
Grief	Dryness	Lungs
Obsession	Humid	Spleen
Fear	Cold	Kidneys

The unsavoury emotions that still engage the mind today were clearly flourishing back in the days of Lao-tzu, who is quite specific about the dangers of losing sight of the 'Middle', as seen in the following verse:

The five colours blind the eye.
The five notes dull the ear.
The five tastes fatigue the mouth.
Riding and hunting
Madden the mind.
Rare treasures hinder right conduct.
Therefore the sage looks
Inward to the centre
And not outward through the eyes.

– Lao-tzu[4]

The Old Master's bewildering insights into human frailties and his appreciation of the Middle Path are recorded here for posterity. Therefore, it is befitting to provide a brief analysis of his venerable words.

'The five colours blind the eyes.'

People who are drawn to the bright lights can become intoxicated by their synthetic energy and thus blinded to the consequences of their own and other's actions. This is one way to consider *blindness*; the other is when the eyes are exposed to the 'extremes' warned of previously. For example, maximum Yang is when a person stares at the sun or a live arc welding kit for a few minutes without protective glasses, both resulting in partial or full loss of sight.

The other extreme is maximum Yin, when the eyes are immersed into pitch-blackness, which considerably impairs the vision although to a much lesser degree than extreme light exposure, when reintroduced to normal lighting conditions — although blindness would follow if the eyes were starved of light for too long.

'The five notes dull the ears.'

Along with the bright lights comes loud music and the distorted views of those who are already intoxicated. The music will damage the inner ear resulting in deafness, while listening to those who have wandered off the Middle Path leads the mind to switch off the hearing to sense and reason.

'The five tastes fatigue the mouth.'

See Dietary Factors.

'Riding and hunting madden the mind.'

How often have people made reference to 'a pack of wolves mentality', when venting their outrage at a gang of thugs attacking a defenceless person? Acting alone, the rational wisdom mind lies closer to the centre, but put the same person in the middle of a rampaging mob and the emotional mind takes precedence. The thirst for power so prevalent during Lao-tzu's time, no doubt influenced this quotation.

'Rare treasures hinder right conduct.'

One of the most harmful weaknesses of humankind is the desire for wealth and all its trappings. Materialistic attitudes fed by craving can make people do untold harm to themselves and others, as their greed rises like a toxic cloud to smother rational thinking.

'Therefore the sage looks inward and not outward through the eyes'

Here the great master philosopher makes clear reference to the Middle Path as being the preferred way. He talks of avoiding what the eyes are seeing and listening instead to the inner Tao, which is the inbuilt compass on the Middle Path Way.

Extreme Fitness

It has for too long been a misguided perception that being fit must also mean being healthy.

'In the drive for "ultimate fitness", health has taken the back seat.' This was a comment from the lips of a senior lecturer in sports science, at one of the country's leading universities, which is currently researching into this problem. Their commission came from the governing body for athletics in the UK, who are concerned by the growing number of athletes consistently battling with physical injuries (Yang) and immune system irregularities (Yin). This problem is by no means just restricted to athletes; all sports people, professional and amateur alike, are afflicted by the same phenomenon and therefore now is a good time to analyse their plight from a Middle Path perspective.

Definitions:

- ***Fitness*** = To Be Physically Fit.
- ***Health*** = In Good Physical or Mental Condition.

As can be seen from these definitions, the western perception of fitness restricts itself to the external (Yang) physical aspect, while interestingly enough, the definition of *healthy* embraces both physical (Yang) and mental/emotional (Yin) aspects. It has for too long been assumed that a physically fit person must automatically be healthy. This presumption has been painfully proven wrong by the many fitness fanatics who have developed serious health problems, or even worse, died prematurely.

Only recently, news of the death of a young and powerful Scandinavian contestant in the televised competition 'The World's Strongest Man' shocked viewers, who had just seen him straining every sinew in his unsuccessful attempt to lift the prestigious crown. The Taoist Middle Path interpretation of his sad demise would be that in his quest to achieve his goal, he walked too long in the hazardous zone of extreme Yang, where the physical demands on his body (External) caused irreparable damage to his organs (Internal).

Inordinately excessive physical training with emphasis on maximising muscular strength has to be supported by an equally inordinate amount of food. Additionally, the muscle bulk required by these sportsmen and women puts a great deal of pressure on the heart to service its mass with oxygen-enriched blood.

An analogy for this would be to compare the heart to a central heating pump, designed to work efficiently when it services, for example, seven or eight radiators. If, however, at a later date it is decided to add another five radiators on to the system, the extra strain on the pump motor will halve its life expectancy.

Those who choose to pursue a path of extreme exercise will find their internal physiology is likewise thrown out of balance. A condition encouraged all the more by 'feel good' chemicals released by the brain, creating a euphoric sense of being, which potentially can mask tissue damage.

Therefore, cognisant of the Taoist doctrine of 'No Extremes', it is not unreasonable to surmise that those who drive themselves too hard have drifted off the Middle Path. In their efforts to achieve match, tournament or competition fitness, they often place themselves in the hands of Yang-driven trainers/coaches, who, when they are asked by their wards: 'What must I do to achieve greatness?' reply, 'Push yourself to your limits and beyond'. And so a regime commences which regularly pushes their bodies into distress, as cardiovascular and respiratory systems go into overload (extreme Yang). Some may even have to hold down demanding jobs (Yang), which all adds to the picture of a body now dominated both internally and externally by Yang.

In the context of Taoism, there is a more sensible approach, which is 'seeking fitness through health'. This entails patiently laying a foundation based on Middle Path principles, designed to create conditions in mind and body conducive to long-term fitness:

1) Think long term in achieving the desired level of fitness; forced fitness cannot be sustained.

2) Review and if necessary realign the skeletal frame with gravity, which frees the lungs to operate more efficiently. (*See Breathing Essentials.*)

3) Eliminate the source of stress triggers; a body with low stress levels can absorb oxygen into its tissues far more efficiently. (*See Stress and Its Dangers.*)

4) Review dietary habits to secure nutritional balance. (*See Dietary Factors.*)

5) Take time out to find the 'spiritual centre' through meditation, to open up the body's energy and mind potential for performance and recovery.

By laying this foundation, the muscles and organs become oxygen efficient, thus lowering the potential for the hazardous to health exhaustion condition. With the aid of Taoist breathing training to supplement this advice, the body's inhalation and (just as important) exhalation functions are maximised, raising performance levels and protecting health.

Health Benefits of Tai Chi Chuan Practice

Benefits

The following is a comprehensive view of specific health benefits attributed to Tai Chi Chuan complete with the considered opinions of two health-industry professionals.

Health Improvements

Tai Chi Chuan stimulates the mind and body to relax and therefore removes the deep-rooted tension associated with hypertension, by encouraging the capillaries to dilate, which takes pressure off the heart.

It removes toxins from the joints, organs and channels through its 'inner cleansing' properties.

It aligns the skeletal structure to operate in harmony with gravity, which keeps gravity's damaging forces working safely through the centre of the joints.

The mental concentration demanded is believed to stimulate the cerebral cortex, helping rebalance emotions and having a positive effect on the treatment of certain nervous disorders.

The lower abdominal and total torso breathing approach energises all organs and support-tissues with oxygen-enriched blood, reducing the likelihood of cancer.

Fatty tissue is broken down through its 'total body' method of practice: no part of the body is without stimulation, even the slightest of movements will involve every joint, tendon, ligament and muscle, thereby eliminating areas of stagnation where fatty deposits accumulate.

The five senses: taste, touch, smell, sight and hearing, all receive a boost, due to the increased Qi circulating through meridians that service these functions, and continued practice will open the 'sixth sense'.

There are noticeable improvements to the immune system, resulting in the gradual diminishment of bacterial and viral infections that would otherwise invade a weaker body.

Sufferers of stomach complaints, such as ulcers or general heartburn, will experience a reduction in levels of damaging acids, often the cause of ulceration and discomfort. The digestive system in general becomes more efficient, which in itself will resolve the excess acid problem.

Those who suffer from asthma will see a reduction in the frequency of attacks, as stress levels drop and lung function improves.

Skin tone and texture improves as Qi levels build in the body.

Regular practice raises the *Shen* (Spirit) and maintains it at a constant level. This keeps the emotions in check and strengthens the immune system.

There will be an interesting increase in stamina, not just in the length of time one can sustain exercise, but also in mental powers (*such as the period of time possible to stay mentally focussed*).

Tests in China have discovered that sustained practice increases the white and red blood cell count. Also, the protein levels of the red cells increase, which helps to sustain health.

The soft rhythmic movements assist the lymphatic fluids to flow throughout the system, thus increasing the potential for detoxification of the body. This also applies to the endocrine (glandular) system as a whole. The *endocrine system* produces chemicals called hormones that are essential for internal balance.

Its associated deep relaxed breathing methods bring a sense of calmness to body and mind, maintain the oxygen levels in the cells, improve the efficiency of the equally important outward breath and gently massage the abdominal organs.

Professional Opinions

There is little doubt that many of the illnesses and diseases experienced nowadays are linked to, or caused by, the stresses and strains of daily living. Many days are lost off work or even school due to stress-related illness and increasing pressures on individuals to achieve. Tai Chi Chuan and Qigong are excellent ways to de-stress and relax both mind and body. The exercises can be enjoyed by people of every age and ability and many of them can be adapted to accommodate people with disabilities. Young and old alike can exercise in harmony and reap the benefits. The philosophy of Yin and Yang with an emphasis on balance and achieving the Middle Path is extremely useful, both in terms of psychologically balancing positive and negative and avoiding extremes.

As a Tai Chi Chuan novice, I personally find my hour-long weekly session a big stress reliever and I get great pleasure in learning each new part of the 'form'. Even as a beginner, one undoubtedly benefits from improved flexibility and coordination through the exercises and greater awareness of one's body position in space.

In short, Tai Chi Chuan and Qigong are holistic forms of exercise that I would recommend to everyone whatever their age, ability or state of health.'

Dr Geraldine Manning
Bsc MB ChB DCCH MRCGP

My first experience of Tai Chi Chuan occurred in Singapore ten years ago. I was working in a heart and lung surgery unit. In the unit, it became apparent that there were certain people who progressed much faster and with fewer complications than others. The common factor appeared to be that they all practised Tai Chi Chuan.

I never thought any more about it until I was working back in England, where I specialised in care of the elderly. Whilst researching into falls in the elderly I came across evidence that indicated that Tai Chi Chuan is one of the most effective interventions into reducing falls.

I have been attending Tai Chi Chuan classes for one year now and I can personally vouch for the benefits of Tai Chi Chuan for general health and wellbeing. The main benefits I have felt are the improvements in my posture and muscle control. After a session you feel that you have had a good workout, but that you are also relaxed. Tai Chi Chuan also works on improving co-ordination and muscle imbalance. Muscle imbalance is a major cause of chronic problems such as lower back pain and this is an excellent way of addressing this problem.

Sylvia Tomassen
Grad. Dip. Phys. MCSP.

Breathing Essentials

If air is Qi and Qi is life,
Then nurture, draw and live.

– PTN

Benefits of Correct Breathing

To highlight the importance of correct breathing and finding the 'centre' of one's being, here is a list of fundamental benefits:

- Brings essential oxygen to all tissues in the body.

- Expels harmful toxins from the body.
- Is the source of the energy that has the most impact on body function.
- Helps regulate the blood pressure.
- Releases stress and can bring about a sense of calm.
- Is the source of great martial power and focus.
- Helps regulate the heart.
- Improves the digestive function.
- Adapts naturally to support a person during emotional or dangerous situations.
- Its rhythmic ebb and flow ripples throughout the length of the torso, gently massages the internal organs.
- In the unborn child, lower abdominal breathing is initiated through the umbilical cord, which is the precursor to breathing air outside the mother's womb.
- It greets the baby at birth.

Dangers of Impaired Breathing

Breathing is bestowed as a gift from the Tao and those who respect and nurture it go on to lead a healthy and long life. But when people choose to ignore its unselfish function and put obstacles in its path, the consequences can be dire. While the positive health-enhancing properties of correct breathing (*Yang*) are many, the negative, harmful effects of a breathing function impaired by ignorance (*Yin*) will be just as numerous and the exact opposite of these benefits.

Impaired breathing:

- Lowers the amount of oxygenated blood reaching the tissues.
- Causes toxins to build up in the body.
- Lowers the energy levels.
- Adversely affects the blood pressure.

- Compounds stress.
- Reduces focus and martial prowess.
- Loads pressure on the heart function.
- Causes the digestive system to work less efficiently.
- If the correct breathing is ignored, its health protecting properties will dissipate even in a young child, and when called upon to assist in a crisis or emotional turmoil, it will fail to support.
- A high-chest 'shallow' breathing pattern offers no internal massage of the organs, which go on to suffer stagnation. (This includes the lower portions of the lungs.)
- It deserts its post at death.

Maxim for Correct Breathing

The ancients knew only too well the importance of correct breathing, as illustrated beautifully in this classical Taoist maxim:

An ignorant man breathes from the chest.
A wise man breathes from the centre.
But enlightened is the man who breathes through the heels.

This needs breaking down into its component parts to bring true clarity to its meaning.

An ignorant man breathes from the chest:

It is important to add to this maxim the Taoist view on the correct breathing method, which is through the nose primarily, and through the mouth only as a secondary backup to the primary, as and when the body dictates. This first line therefore, represents the perpetual mouth breather, who falls into the trap of 'high chest breathing'. This unfortunately common method of breathing is notorious in traditional Chinese medicine for starving the lower portions of the lungs and damaging the tissues by seriously restricting efficiency in both inhalation and exhalation.

A wise man breathes from the centre:

The 'centre' in respect of respiration refers to the abdomen, where the Real Dan Tien resides. In traditional Chinese medicine, martial arts and spiritual training, lower abdominal breathing is actively promoted for the following reasons:

1) To release the diaphragm and thus improve the lung function.

2) To stimulate the organs by the gentle internal rhythmic movement of the stomach/abdominal muscles and diaphragm.

3) To tap into the centre of the power used in martial arts.

4) To create the process in the area of the Real Dan Tien that kick-starts the internal route to enlightenment.

An enlightened man breathes from his heels:

This reference to the heels means to sink the Qi, because in internal training a downwards sinking of the weight into the heels earths the Qi to provide a strong root and good leg circulation. The term *enlightened*, equates to 'Grand Circulation', which is the result of sinking the Qi to not only the heels, but also the Yong chuan points on the soles of the feet and throughout the body generally.

Smoking

Grey serpents grow within our minds
To control all sense and reason.

– PTN

The unfathomable way smokers ignore all the hard medical facts, which list the crippling and potentially fatal diseases that spring from the substances found in a cigarette, is for non-smokers bewildering. Even when the extremes hit and life is threatened, they still reach out for another, against 'all sense and reason'.

In relation to the breathing function, a sad side effect of smoking is how it actively encourages high-chest shallow breathing through requiring the smoker to draw smoke and air in through the mouth. This in itself creates a lower vital oxygen intake, but when it is also polluted with toxic smoke then the results are, in the long term, catastrophic to human health.

Stress and its Dangers

In the past, people, from a very early age, instinctively followed prevailing behaviour patterns that were imposed by societies throughout the world. The severity of these 'life rules' differed from country to country; however, whether a conformist path led to a long and healthy existence or an early grave was irrelevant to those who conducted the orchestrations.

An example of this would have been the coalminer's son, who upon leaving school was expected to follow in his father's footsteps. This was despite the fact that numerous fellow miners had been forced to retire early and then died through 'industrial disease'. Probably out of respect for his elders and blind ignorance, the son would have accepted his lot and ploughed on. Before too long, he would have become fully initiated into the family's and society's traditions and would encourage his sons to continue in his footsteps — and so the cycle continued.

This was particularly prevalent during the Victorian period and sadly continues, though much diluted, to this day. The three pivotal protagonists propagating this ignorance were/are: families, institutions and politicians. All played their part in the creation of a 'sick' society and it will take their combined efforts to put things right.

In light of this knowledge, it is sobering to consider where the world would be without the 'nonconforming souls' who broke out of the system and emerged with their eyes raised to the heavens asking 'What's it all about?' 'Why are we here?' 'Why do we behave like this?' And 'Is there something I could be doing which is better?'

Poor health is a major industry, generating billions of pounds for the manufacturers of medicines and for private healthcare, whose collective motto surely must be 'Sick people are big business'. This in itself explains why the tobacco industry still thrives to this day. These businesses generate massive revenues for their respective governments, so where is the incentive for our leaders to take the initiative and promote healthy life styles?

Stress can kill and in fact does kill a great number of people, despite their death certificates stating something else. The practice of the western world's health officials is to name only that which directly caused the death, ignoring totally the causes leading to it. A step in the direction of honesty and clarity would be a death certificate that reads as follows:

Cause of Death: **Working in a high-pressure environment for 25 years, keeping long hours at the office and failing to find an effective method to relieve the mental and physical stress this caused.**

Stress Symptoms

The trouble is, the majority of stressed out people do not realise they are suffering until some kind of physical or emotional breakdown occurs. For the benefit of those who may be potential candidates, listed below are some typical side effects of stress:

- Short tempered
- High blood pressure
- Palpitations of the heart
- Shortness of breath
- Erratic sleep patterns
- Inability to cope
- Muscle aches and pains
- Loss of appetite
- General lethargy
- Cycle of colds and flu viruses
- Digestion problems
- Irregular bowel movement
- Onset of dermatitis
- Weight loss
- Weight gain
- Loss of sustained concentration
- Emotional swings

- Headaches and migraines
- Nose bleeds
- Asthma attacks
- Facial ticks/twitches
- Speech problems
- Memory loss
- Hair loss

There are 24 in total, but the list could have gone on and knowing this, just think of the improvements to life simply by eliminating stress.

Stress-Free Benefits

At Work

- Improved concentration
- More output
- Higher attendance
- More confidence
- Cope better with workload
- Better quality work

At Home:

- More relaxed sleep
- Increased stamina for housework and play
- Balanced appetite
- More tolerant with loved ones

In closing, this message is for those who turn to drugs (including cigarettes and alcohol) in the search for relief from stress: the false comfort that these debilitating habits bring cannot be compared to the freedom and protection offered by the Middle Path.

Dietary Factors

This highly charged and contentious subject cannot be ignored in the search for the Middle Path. The Chinese knowledge of foods and herbs is a science in its own right and this section is intended to offer an insight into how adopting balanced Middle Path dietary habits will enhance health 'from the inside'.

Extreme Eating and Dieting

In terms of self-inflicted extremes obesity (Yang) sits at one end and anorexia (Yin) at the other. Each is in its own unique way as bad as the other, because their end results are the same — premature death.

One should consume no more than
Is necessary to maintain health.

– Taoist Precept

The mental processes that drive people to these extremes are born from blind obsession. Whether obsessed with gluttony or with abstinence, sufferers (and they do suffer) become blind to the adverse effects these conditions inflict on their bodies.

Stop eating before the stomach is full.

– Taoist Precept

At the root of this obsessive behaviour skulks a major emotional by-product of the negative force of Yin — 'low esteem'. The causes must be placed firmly at the feet of a modern society, which, in general, subscribes to a warped doctrine of slim is beautiful and anything else is unacceptable.

When people cannot live up to society's expectations, they are engulfed by a sense of failure, depleting their self-worth and lowering their spirit/willpower. Unlike Buddha, who consciously chose to walk the uneven path of extreme dieting, the majority slide towards obesity or anorexia, almost oblivious to the fact, and that is despite friends and family telling them in no uncertain terms as to where they are going wrong.

Another cause, although not the primary one, is the regularly spewed out garbage from the so-called food experts, incessantly claiming and then contradicting each other's findings. How are the public expected to settle on dependable and nutritious diets, when those they look to for guidance cannot agree?

A maxim that has for years been tripping off the tongues of people concerned over eating habits is 'You are what you eat!' (or don't eat in the case of anorexia). At both ends of the eating disorder spectrum, there is yet another common thread, the fact that both the obese and the anorexic can be starved of essential nutrition.

Intolerances

Under this category lies the unsavoury fast foods, the facts of which most people, thankfully, already know, but it is the less well-known world of intolerances that will now be singled out as a silent but deadly cause of nutritional starvation.

This is the most misunderstood and under-reported area of food culture, one that the food industry is happy to brush under the rug. Every time a manufacturer has to extract a harmful filler from their products, it eats into their sacred margins. That a particularly nasty additive is causing untold discomfort to their customers in the forms of irritable bowel, wheezy chest, nausea, tiredness and dermatological reactions, to name but a few, is of no concern to them.

An extreme example of this occurred with Acute Peanut Allergy, where people had to die before the manufacturers acted by labelling the packaging with warnings. Daily, consumers are exposed to a cocktail of toxic chemicals, which include antibiotics, fertilizers, insecticides, food colours, preservatives and enhancers. In isolation each chemical might well have little or no detrimental effect on the body, but collectively, they are being blamed for contributing to the emergence of ME (myalgic encephalomyelitis, where stress, plus ingested chemical pollutants now seems the likely cause), General Immune Deficiency (which accounts for the inexplicable rise in viral infections) and hyperactivity and aggressive behavioural problems in children.

The Middle Path Diet

From the perspective of the Middle Path, what does all this mean in practical terms? If diet is one of the major contributory factors in the decline of health, then the remedy lies in the choice of food.

The ancients knew how to sow, grow, prepare and cook food to maximise its nutritional potential. In contrast, present-day western society has for too long relied upon the misleading claims of the mass food producers, who assure the public their food is healthy but whose claims are regularly shown to be misleading.

When someone was showing deficiency in their vital Qi, the ancient Chinese, according to the *Nei Ching (The Classic Book of Internal Medicine),* would, as a matter of course, seek to replenish it first and foremost with a review of the patient's diet.

If too much food is eaten, the breath
and psychic centres will be obstructed.

– Taoist Precept

The modern western approach to learning how to cook is to study the basic nutritional content of the product alongside a multitude of ways to both cook and present the dish. The Chinese, however, look much deeper by appreciating its medicinal properties, spending less time on presentation and more on preparation to help the food retain its Qi. For example, steaming is the preferred way to cook vegetables and fish, as it retains more of their nutrients. Roasting meat is to be avoided as this holds unnecessary fat. Meat quickly fried in smoking-hot oil, however, produces less fat while retaining its texture.

In addition, Chinese cooks categorise food into two distinct groups: the Yin and the Yang, then subcategorise them into 'five tastes', based on the Five Elements and their corresponding organs: these are Water = Kidneys = Salty (Yin); Wood = Liver = Sour (Yin); Fire = Heart = Bitter (Yin); Earth = Spleen = Sweet (Yang) and Metal = Lungs = Pungent (Yang). If therefore, any of the five tastes are taken singularly in excess, they will damage the organ they would normally balance.

Traditional Chinese medicine suggests that by applying the correct blend of these foods depending on the condition of the patient, and adjusting the mix to suit the seasonal time of the year, a healthy and healing Middle Path diet appears.

When Lao-tzu stated 'The five tastes fatigue the mouth', he is believed to have meant excessive taste. For example, when a person develops a particular taste for, let's say, garlic (Pungent): so strong and enveloping is its taste, that besides repelling all known life in the immediate vicinity with its repugnant odours, the joyous subtle flavours of other foods and drinks are cloaked by its intensity. In other words, the four other taste receptors will become suppressed as one becomes predominant over the rest.

Yin and Yang Food

The Chinese have developed a sophisticated view of food that goes far beyond the equivalent western understanding, which pays minimal attention to its health promoting properties and more to how it can be processed and packaged to offer a greater return for shareholders. The result of this is seen in the food-related health problems it *causes* rather than alleviates.

The Chinese way, which has evolved over thousands of years, is to view food from the angle of its intrinsic Qi and how that Qi can be absorbed to bring about balance in the body of the consumer. Taoist food science is extensive in both its depth and breadth of coverage and therefore, only a brief but relevant cross-section will be discussed.

In China, food has been split into five distinct categories, each identified by the food's natural occurring energy essence. (The following table, while by no means a full listing, is detailed enough to give a basic understanding of how the categories work.)

Depending on the category of the health-debilitating condition, a traditional Chinese doctor/herbalist will prescribe certain teas, herbs and foods to counter its negative effects. For example, someone with a chill on the kidneys will be advised to consume food which is categorised as warm or hot to strengthen the Yang and suppress the Yin. If an organ is diagnosed as needing a tonic, the doctor/herbalist may recommend the patient eat the corresponding organ of an ox, sheep or chicken. This is because it is believed that kidney benefits the kidneys and liver benefits the liver.

Yin		Middle Path	
Cold	*Cool*	*Neutral*	
Tomato	Millet	Pork	Potato
Water Melon	Lettuce	Corn	Peanut
Banana	Rape	Quail	Sweet Potato
Cucumber	Celery	Carrot	Cabbage
Sugarcane	Pear	Grape	Honey
Bamboo Shoot	Tea	Beef	Mushroom
Water Chestnut	Apple	Milk	Rice
Wild Rice	Wheat	Herring	Mackerel
Crab	Mung Bean	Oyster	Sardine
Salt	Bean Curd	Tuna	White Fish
Octopus	Buckwheat	Duck	Lamb
Radish	Barley	Egg	Almond
Asparagus	Tangerine	Coconut	Fig
Grapefruit	Bean	Olive	Pineapple
Star Fruit	Spinach	Plum	Raspberry
	Water Cress	Beet	Peas
	Peppermint	Turnip	Yam
	Marjoram	White Sugar	

TABLE 3. YIN AND YANG FOOD CATEGORIES

Yang

Warm	*Hot*
Peach	Curry
Ginger	Black Pepper
Onion	Pepper
Garlic	Trout
Wie	Chilli
Chesnut	Ginseng
Walnut	
Lobster	
Chicken	
Mutton	
Pig's Liver	
Eel	
Cherry	
Vinegar	
Pumpkin	
Kidney Bean	
Anchovy	
Mussel	
Shrimp	
Kidney	
Butter	
Strawberry	
Leek	
Brown Sugar	
Mustard	
Basil	
Rosemary	
Nutmeg	
Coriander	
Fennel Seed	
Pine Nut	

Other Taoist Precepts

'Those who eat at night will lose one day of life.'

Going to bed with a heavy meal in the stomach puts a tremendous strain on the whole digestive system, because nature tends to shut the digestion factory down overnight and, therefore, this is its weakest period of efficiency. Life may be shortened by an imbalance to the biorhythms generated by poor quality sleep, indigestion, tiredness, toxin build-up and an unhealthy fluctuating demand for food.

'Those who got to bed drunk at night will lose one month of life.'

Lying in bed with an excess of alcohol (*and its associated chemicals*) swimming around the system also stresses the digestion process. And because it is not working to its desired level of efficiency, the alcohol lingers in the body longer causing more damage than it would when a person is animated during the daytime.

'Regulate fluid intake so that urination does not exceed more than four times in a day.'

The simple rule to follow with this is to find the balance: in the summer the body requires more fluids than it does in the winter; therefore, seasonal variations in the frequency of bladder releases will occur. Drink when thirsty and listen to the inner Tao; it will signal when to stop. The same applies to urination, when the urge to go surfaces, do not ignore the impulse, otherwise subtle bladder and urinary tract infections could emerge.

PART THREE

'Some people are not content with destroying their body,
They will even attack their eternal spirit.

—PTN

Introduction to Part Three

Visions of Metaphysical Realms

The next four chapters consider metaphysics and visions, not clear, hard scientific fact. The insights contained are intended to help budding adepts gauge how far along the Middle Path they have come and to aid them in unravelling the sometimes incomprehensible and conflicting claims of a subject steeped in myth and legend.

These four chapters commence with an explanation of the *centres* and the meaning of being *centred* in life, body and mind (without such knowledge, the higher reaches of the Path would otherwise remain vague). With the aid and guidance of a teacher formally trained in the esoteric aspects of Taoism, the evolved student will be led safely along the Middle Path to its centre. It is at this point the chronicle ends, but for the happy traveller a new cycle of discovery is just beginning.

Chapter Seven
Physical and Spiritual Centres

Before I go much further
I'll leave a note behind,
Containing information
That could 'centre' all mankind

– PTN

So what do the ancient sages mean by the *centre*? Spiritual cultivators will say 'It is the centre of the spiritual being.' Martial arts advocates will say 'It is the centre of power and gravity focussed in the waist.' Health purveyors will say 'It is the point in the core of the body where the breath should be sunk to.' So who is right? Well, they all are. Here is an elaboration on each of their views.

The Centres

Spiritual Centre

The spirit-body is the real person, the ethereal substance that occupies the physical body and naturally gravitates to its centre. It is Yin in form, yet the bearer and creator of Yang: it energises the cells of the Yang physical form to create life. Chapter 10 analyses its cultivation in detail; however, for the purpose of this synopsis, it is sufficient to say that without the sense of this centre all the other pieces of the jigsaw would never fit.

Gravitational Centre

The martial artists tend to concentrate more on the waist than other areas of the body, simply because they rightly believe it is from the waist that true power is derived. Over the centuries, they also discovered that by focusing a portion of their attention on the Real Dan Tien, which lies at the core of the pelvic basin and roughly in line with the top of the illiac crests (*see Fig. 7*), rooting, coordination and balance are all improved. And the reason for this is that the Real Dan Tien is the centre of gravity for the whole body and, once located, can be nurtured to create the quite astounding feats of physical agility seen by many nowadays as performed by the awesome monks from Shaolin.

When this centre is acquired gravitationally and spiritually, then the adept has achieved 'Central Equilibrium' (*Tsung Tien*). Another name given for this desired condition is 'Silk Reeling Energy' (*Chan Su Chin)*, which is when gravity is centred throughout all joints and energy (*Qi*) is coordinated from feet to fingertips.

Power starts in the feet, journeys to the legs,
Is accelerated and directed by the waist and
Bursts forth into the fingers.

– Tai Chi Maxim.

Health Centre

The astounding benefits that reverberate from the relatively simple process of sinking the breath down to the Real Dan Tien explains why the Chinese regard the opening of this centre as being the most important in the promotion of health. Figure 7 locates and shows the order of progressive development to open the energy, axial, gravitational and spiritual centres:

Figure 7 — Major Centres
Cultivation Sequence

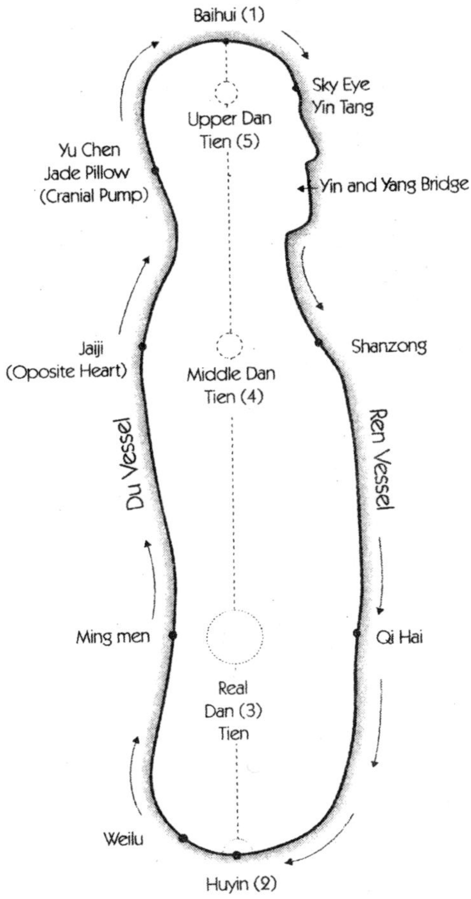

1: The Baihui point is known as the 'Heaven's Gate' or the 'Hundred Convergences'; it is where the soul is believed to take its leave from the body on its journey to the next existence. It is the most Yang of all 'cavities' (acupuncture points) and if it is kept where it should be, that is, facing upward to the heavens, all below it stays in order.

2: The Huiyin point is located at the centre of the pelvic floor and vertically in line with the Baihui. When these two major cavities are aligned they open the Chung Mei, a central core stabilising channel which is linked to the kidneys and helps keep both Ren (Yin) and Du (Yang) meridians balanced. The Huiyin is known as the 'Yin meeting place' or 'Yin convergence' and, as its name implies, is the most Yin of the cavities. If kept naturally hanging down pointing to earth (this is accomplished only when the Weilu is employed to do the same), it keeps the energy in the legs and the kidneys strong, while aligning the lower back to relieve undue pressure on the joints.

3: The Real Dan Tien, as mentioned previously, is the centre of gravity for the whole body and the direct axial pivoting point through which all movements must be channelled. Only when (1) and (2) align, will it be possible to find the 'real' centre. It is also classified as the major storage vessel for Qi, giving credence to its other name, which is the 'sea of energy'. The Real Dan Ten is balanced by the Ming men on the spine and the Qihai on the abdomen.

4: The Middle Dan Tien is the centre of gravity for the upper body and regarded as the root of the shoulders and arms. Through its front (Shanzong) and back (Jaiji) gates, Qi is fed to and released from the heart and indirectly the lungs, to keep them functioning in a healthy manner. Spiritually, it is believed to be the original residence of the spirit, or soul from where if cultivated it ascends to the next level.

5: The Upper Dan Tien, or 'Third Eye', is where the spirit is concentrated to create the Shen Crystal (*see Chapter 9*), which gives rise to awakening psychic potential. It lies at a point midway between the 'Front Gate' (Sky Eye of Yintang) and the 'Rear Gate' (Yu chen). It is the centre of gravity in the head. Its location corresponds to that of the pineal glad. An interesting observation is the Oxford Dictionary's anatomical explanation of the axis point of the head, as being located at the… 'second cervical vertebra'. This is precisely the place the Chinese call the Yuchen ('Jade Pillow') point, that acts as a cerebral pump to propel the refined Qi around the torso meridian circuitry and outward to the hands. (NB: it also influences the Qi returning back to the torso).

This, therefore, is the suggested sequence to inner clarity created by the gradual assimilation of these magical centres into the human consciousness.

When the spirit centre (true centre) opens (like a lift shaft), it is through 'this vertical portal' that lies the road to enlightenment.

Progression to the highest plane is
Subject to successfully negotiating
The stepping-stones into the true centre.

– PTN

'But how do I know that I have found the true centre?' This is a sensible question to ask, and the answer can be found in Chapter 9 under 'Tai Chi Sung'.

Meditation Practice: Connecting the Centres

Having located the centre of gravity within the physical body, the next stage is to establish its connection to the spirit-body and this can only be achieved through the process of meditation. Taoist meditation is an integral part of Tai Chi Chuan and is the method of regulating breathing, Qi and Shen; in other words it is essential to the cultivation of health and spiritual enlightenment. There are three methods of application: Standing, Sitting and Moving, which will be discussed after first viewing the preparation necessary to achieve good practice.

Preparing to Meditate

1. **Choose the right location:** This is very important because meditation opens up the body to breathe Qi, not only through the nostrils but also through the acupuncture cavities. Under these conditions if the body is placed in an area where negative Qi thrives, then it will absorb this Qi and lose its harmony.

2. **Preliminary exercise and massage:** For best results it is advisable to practise gentle warm-up exercises specifically geared to relax the body; then follow this with self-massage to release any tight spots, especially around the joints.

(See 'Feng Shui of Training' in Chapter 5 for additional preparation advice.)

Three Methods of Meditation

Sitting: In sitting meditation, the arms tend to participate in guiding the Qi to specific locations on the body, or to flow unimpeded along the meridians. Although sitting meditation can be practised in a straight-backed chair with feet set shoulder-width apart, the most common method is the cross-legged posture in which the buttocks are placed on a cushion to raise the hips higher than the knees for good lumbar alignment. By crossing the legs, the Qi is focussed into the torso/head circuit, which is the most desirable for training the 'Small Heavenly Cycle' (*see Chapter 9*).

Note! Cross-legged training should be undertaken with caution. Never fold the legs up so tightly that the circulation becomes obstructed.

Standing: In standing meditation the Chinese say 'You must stand tall and be rooted to the ground like a tree'. The most common methods are when feet are to be placed shoulder-width apart with the insteps parallel and the legs structured either straight or in a squatting position. If the legs are straight the knees should not be pushed back against the joints, instead they should be positioned centrally for correct Middle Path alignment. When squatting, the knees should not be bent to project out beyond the toes; otherwise the central gravity line of the body becomes compromised. Although there are many other variations of standing meditation, the two mentioned are the most suited for beginners.

Note! While both sitting and standing styles are to be practised, standing is regarded as slightly more advanced because it develops the foundation for 'Grand Circulation'. Also, as a point of caution, avoid excessive sitting meditation, as this can weaken the legs.

Moving Meditation: This is in fact another way to describe the art of Tai Chi Chuan, where the mind, spirit and body unite into a single flowing energy wave otherwise known in Taoist circles as 'Grand Circulation' or Tai Chi Sung. The enlightened conditions present in the body when moving meditation has been mastered is in most Taoist circles a much sought after goal, because besides the well-documented spiritual uplift, the health of the individual reaches its pinnacle. While the feet still leave tracks on the Earth the total state of emptiness that moving meditation delivers is true enlightenment in both the physical and spiritual sense, but when the body dies, the cultivated spirit achieves enlightenment in the spiritual sense.

The key conditions that must be nurtured to create untainted moving meditation are:

- Empty Mind
- Stilled Spirit
- Structurally Aligned Body
- A Good Physically Conditioned Body
- Maximum Efficiency in Respiratory Function
- Complete Harmony of all the Above

Typical Meditation Session

The following describes a good meditation practice that is suitable for a beginner in sitting or standing styles. It assumes that the person has established good posture in the chosen style (*see Fig. 7 to locate points*):

Rest the eyelids, do not completely shut them.

Lift the head up from the Baihui point to straighten the torso and neck and free the diaphragm.

Place the tongue on the roof of the mouth and with its tip touch lightly behind the two upper front teeth; this forms the connecting bridge for the Du and Ren channels.

Breathe in and out through the nose, training the breath to gently sink down and inflate the abdomen.

Place both hands with palms facing in over the Qihai point located directly below the navel. Note: Women should place left hand over right and men the reverse.

Gently sink the breath to where the hands are now placed, creating a sense of expansion and contraction throughout the whole pelvic basin.

Empty the mind of any distracting thoughts, leaving only the soft cyclic sounds of the breathing in the consciousness.

Keep the upper and lower teeth lightly touching, and linked to an outward breath swallow any accumulated saliva.

Allow the mind to drift to a special place halfway between sleeping and waking. This is the location of the inner peace that once discovered can be returned to, refreshing body, mind and spirit.

A Centred Lifestyle

An earlier chapter considered the importance of finding the Middle Path in life generally; for without this achievement obstacles will continuously be placed in the way to enlightenment. If, however, the centre still remains elusive, here are some key pointers to follow in helping locate it.

At Work

A job with little mental stimulation, boring repetition, unfriendly colleagues, long hours for little reward, little or no appreciation shown, unhealthy working environment, long distance to travel to and from work, unnecessary pressures imposed by disorganised management, no career prospects = *STRESS*!!! So, CHANGE THE JOB! Nobody is irreplaceable; the business will happily continue to blunder on long after the dejected soul has left, until that is, the decision-makers themselves 'see the light' (hopefully by reading this book) and improve working conditions for their most important asset — the workforce.

At Home

How does one know if a home is centred? If the guidance given in the previous chapters has been followed, the home should be a happy place to return to. When harmony is achieved between building and occupants, then they have found the centre or Middle Path. In addition, if there is discord within a family, 'seek the centre through the mother.' The mother *is* the centre of a family unit. Make her life more enjoyable by giving her some space, respecting her views and following her directions; for within her make-up are latent Feng Shui skills, which if allowed to flow, will pour forth to create the Middle Path of the home.

Chapter Eight

The Six Jade Steps of Tai Chi Chuan

Oh wondrous stone, this crown of Earth,
What secrets you could tell,
Of Emperors and heroes,
Whose fate upon you fell.

– PTN

In China there is a mountain range they call the Jade Mountains; precious are they in the minds of the people and precious is the stone of their namesake. The Six Jade Steps are also special in that they represent the connection between Heaven and Earth; for just like the Jade Mountains they rise from the Earth to touch the Heavens.

The Chinese also consider this rare, beautiful and indestructible stone to have magical and curative properties and for this reason, they believed that by associating their chosen leader with it he would become elevated to 'Supreme Celestial Being'; this explains the title 'Jade Emperor'.

The Six Jade Steps are based on the internal training methods of the Yang style of the Tai Chi Chuan masters of old who discovered that, when their special Yogic Taoist training methods were practised in a specific sequence, enlightenment followed. These are the sequential steps that elevate the student to such heights that it is possible to understand and appreciate the delightful treasures awaiting those who have the patience to search within.

Progress must be on a step-by-step basis, as can be confirmed by those who, lacking the patience required, have attempted to by-pass some of the initial steps only to be disappointed by the result. While the Jade Steps are 'internal' in how they are assimilated, they still must be viewed overall as Yang, in that they are creating the conditions here and now in the physical Earth-bound body. Their role is to open up the potential for the Six Golden Steps which are Yin in classification, as they deal with all matters on the road to enlightenment that are non-physical and intangible, namely: matters of the Spirit (*Shen*).

Step One – Foundation and Posture

The purpose of Step One is to realign the physical body both while in motion and at rest by bringing the gravity line down from the crown of the head like a string of pearls through the centre of the joints. To understand how to practise and assimilate these improvements to the body, it is necessary to separate and analyse each component part of Step One.

Foundation

This collectively means all matters in respect of relief of stiffness in the hips (waist/pelvic girdle), knees, ankles and feet, and postural correctness of the same. As any builder would say, 'A house is only as good as the foundation it sits on', so too is the human body, which relies on leg strength to create upper body stability. In Yin and Yang relevancy, when the legs (including feet, knees and hips) are Yang (strong) the upper body is able to be pliable (*Yin*) and free from stiffness.

This strength comes from opening the senses between the brain and the feet by practising Tai Chi Chuan walking drills and exploring the many associated stances, with emphasis on weight distribution while aligning feet, knees and hips. A fundamental point made here is the importance of knowing exactly where the gravity line should be at any specific time in the feet (and body generally), when either stationary or in motion. For example following the directions below creates a sense of 'Gravitational Rooting' (*see figure 8*):

FIGURE 8
SUBSTANTIAL AND INSUBSTANTIAL IN BOXING STANCE

Starting from a stationary position, when the feet are parallel to each other, shoulder-width apart and the point loading (Middle Path connection point to the Earth) is centred on the Yongchuan points (on the balls of the feet). Lift the toes of the right foot off the ground and pivot the foot 45° outward on the heel, while bending the right knee and transferring the whole body weight over the Yongchuan point, as the toes settle gently on the ground.

This is now the 'substantial' leg over which the hips should now also be set at 45° along the same line as the foot. The centre of the hip, back of the knee and Yongchuan point should all now align. This releases the 'insubstantial' foot to lift and hover approximately 7cm above the ground, toes hanging naturally down, lower than the heel. The foot should be swung gently in towards the right ankle, then out in a curve to step in front, landing on the heel at a convergence point where a straight shoulder-width line meets a 45° line drawn from the toes of the right foot.

By placing the heel of the left foot down first, the Qi pathways open to encourage gravitational force to pour downward into the foot, creating the desired Qi circulation sequence (weight transferring into leg = Qi sinking, and weight withdrawing from leg = Qi floating). Gradually transfer the weight from the right foot into the left foot while turning the hips to face forward. The weight distribution to complete the stance should be 70% in the left and 30% in the right, which will align the tip of the left kneecap vertically over the base of the toes. This is called 'Boxing Stance'.

Posture

This encompasses all corrections made in the 'Foundation', plus the 24 joints of the spine, showing where the body alignment (Middle Path) lies when it is stationary and the controlling centre of a body in flexing motion. In practical terms an example of this is when the Tai Chi Chuan teacher checks that the top of the student's head is maintained at a constant height to the ground, when the body is involved in any directional movement (in other words not bobbing up and down). This ensures the legs are consistently bent to the correct degree, thus stabilising and establishing the physical Middle Path centre line.

SUMMARY

The key benefits of Step One are:

1) It places the feet correctly to give perfect stances.

2) It positions the feet correctly both on and off the ground to encourage the Qi to sink and float upwards respectively.

3) It shows how to align the knees between the feet and the hips whether standing still or in motion.

4) It shows how to 'Drop the Buttocks and Loosen the Waist'.

5) It aligns the joints of the spine to maintain an upright stable posture.

Gravity

She's with us from the day we're born,
Still there when we depart,
Her closeness is unparalleled
For she dwells within our heart.

By heeding all she says and does
A home she'll keep within,
But choose to walk in ignorance
And she'll bend you like a pin.

– PTN

Step Two – Discerning Yin and Yang

The Oxford English Dictionary defines discerning as 'having true insight', which in this case means the observation and analysis of the twin forces of Yin and Yang at work in the human body. Step Two, however, only requires the practitioner to acquire the fundamental basic principles of Yin and Yang in respect of their anatomical classification and activity in the fluid body.

Anatomically, for example, the following are classified as Yin: the face, front of torso, pelvic floor, palms, inner arms, armpits, groin, inside of legs and soles of feet. The forehead, top and back of the head, all the back including the spine, backs of the hands and arms, outside and back of legs and top of the feet, however, are Yang. Furthermore, in respect of relativity (*see Chapter 3*), everything above the Dan Tien is Yang and below is Yin. The outer surface of the body is Yang and all insides are Yin and so on, the permutations are incalculable, however, only a general appreciation is desirable at this stage.

Feeling Yin and Yang

Originally Tai Chi Chuan was conceived as a supreme martial art, and in order for students to clearly feel the two energies flowing in and out of the body, the masters categorised the more physical aspects of Tai Chi Chuan as Yin and Yang:

Yang

Pushing, punching, elbowing, shouldering, head-butting, chopping, finger poking, finger pointing, glaring (eyeing someone aggressively), kicking, stamping, kneeing, tensing, returning, attacking, advertising (intentions), carrying, holding (forcibly controlling).

Yin

Parrying, pulling, adhering, leading, folding, intercepting, catching/ plucking, receiving, defending, disguising (intentions), lifting, holding (leading or redirecting incoming force).

Experiencing these actions through body-motion (through a Tai Chi Chuan form preferably, although not essential) will for the first time deliver a true sense of the two inseparable but opposite energies.

Every time the body moves it requires both Yin and Yang mutually supporting actions, subtly separated at their interface by an invisible line (Middle Path). By establishing a sense of the 'Two', only then is it possible to find the secret that lies at their centre and feel it working to create harmony without either one taking prominence. This is the feeling of the Middle Path or of centre or balance (all meaning the same thing).

Yin and Yang Patterns

Having grasped a sense of Yin and Yang, using the inner consciousness, it should be possible to glean that energy has natural patterns or directions of flow indicated as follows: Forward and upward = Yang. Backward and downward = Yin. Sideways in either direction = Yin/Yang, depending on the circumstances.

When introduced into some basic Tai Chi Chuan or Qigong movements, it is possible to 'Catch the Wave' of these natural rhythms or patterns and surf on their oscillations. Having achieved this, the next step materialises.

Yin Qi and Yang Qi

One rises to the head while
The other sinks to the feet,
Then interchange in places
Where both had planned to meet.

– PTN

Step Three – Yin and Yang Subtlety

This step is also known in Tai Chi Chuan circles as 'Yin and Yang of hands and head', the principle being enhancement of the natural ebb and flow of Qi through two important energy cavities (acupressure points):

1) The Yuchen (Jade Pillar) — Located on the Du Mei (Governor Vessel) at the top of the second cervical vertebrae. It is a powerful Yang meridian point and is also known as the cranial pump.

2) The Yin tang (Sky Eye) — Located on the Ren Mei (Conception Vessel) just slightly lower than the centre of the forehead. As its name implies it is a powerful Yin meridian point and is sometimes called the Third Eye.

Coordinating both of these cavities with movements of the spine, shoulders, arms and hands transforms what would otherwise be sporadic Qi-flow into smooth waves (*see Chapter 9, Step Two*). Qi (energy) naturally flows in spiral wave frequencies and therefore if the pathways (meridians in particular) through which it travels are free from sharp corners, projections and obstructions, a constant flow to all extremities will be enjoyed.

The 'subtly' alluded to in this step refers to internally and externally sensing the creation of gentle wave-like movements in the physical body — movements that become the vehicle for the resultant 'Qi Wave', experienced when the 'Small Heavenly Cycle' has been established. In practical terms this entails linking up in a specific flowing sequence the 'String of Pearls': the spine to shoulder to elbow to wrist to finger joints. And while this wave is in motion the head must accurately coordinate and correspond to this action by gently tilting backward (Yin) and forward (Yang), described in detail as follows:

As the physical wave rises up the spine from the pelvic girdle (brought about by tilting the Weilu under) and reaches the Jaiji location (see fig. 7), the head should tilt up by lifting the chin which hollows the Yuchen (Yin).

From this point onwards the wave undergoes a three-way split, one part continues to rise to the Yuchen while the other two separate and flow into each shoulder respectively. (This slightly elevates and rounds the upper back and shoulders collectively.) From here the wave now sits in anticipation of the next stage of the journey, which is over and through the head, down the arms and out through the hands.

Now raise the Shanzong point at the middle of the chest, while simultaneously sinking both shoulders, followed by the elbows and wrists (in that order). The chest meanwhile should relax and settle centrally (Middle Path) just as the wave bursts forth through the wrists into the hands.

Transformation of the head from Yin into Yang involves the gradual lifting of the Baihui point, while pulling the chin inward throughout the process already described; commencing as the chest begins to rise and arriving in a full Yang (chin in) position as the wave materialises in the fingers (filling out the Yuchen).

Qi Flow

It moves like a wind-driven wave
Through preordained paths we engrave.

— PTN

Step Four – Silk Reeling Energy

The name 'Silk reeling Energy' (Chan Su Chin) describes the incredibly delicate yet potentially powerful spiral actions of a body in motion and the corresponding Qi that circulates through its pathways. In chapter 5 it was established that Qi spirals throughout everything in the universe and it is this aspect of the Earth-stage rejuvenation process that receives consideration here.

This step will concentrate on the creation of a body wave flowing from the feet to the top of the head and down the arms to the fingers. Within this wave must be developed a skill, a skill that brings closer the true workings of Tai Chi Chuan: 'The Spirals of Chan Su Chin'. This twinning force that operates naturally through the skeletal structure is transmitted only via a limited number of uniquely constructed joints: ankles, knees, hips, vertebrae, shoulders, elbows and wrists.

The knees and elbows play a vital role in the twinning process in spite of their limited range of movement (*especially lateral twisting*) compared to the others listed. However they are supported by the gyratory effects of the Tibia and Fibula bones (*for the knees*) and Ulna and Radius (*for the elbows*), as well as the elasticity offered by the muscles, tendons and ligaments.

Each one of these key junctions acts like a cog sequentially coordinating the subtle flow of energy up and down the body. They act like ten interlinked pumping stations (*Yang*) as the Qi journeys upwards from feet to fingers and as mini reservoirs (*Yin*) as it returns back to Earth.

These key stations are in sequential order based on the energy rising off a single leg push against the ground:

1) Heel — Gravity is moved to the centre of the heel which is forced down into the ground in an anticlockwise twisting action (viewed from above). This downward action creates a resultant upward rebounding force (Jing) which spirals upwards to the next station.

2) Knee — Here the knee receives the incoming pulse, interprets its force and direction and propels it upward by aligning with the anticlockwise flow in a combined twisting and straightening action (visually seen as straightening the leg from its initial bent position).

3) Hips — The hip receiving the incoming Jing from the knee also catches the spiral wave intensity and direction, and with the help

of a balancing action in the opposite hip (both hips twinning in an anticlockwise motion) propels it to a central juncture at the base of the spine.

4) Weilu — By the time the Jing has reached this point the Weilu will have moved from its position at the beginning of the chain (tilted under) to hanging naturally down (like a plumb-bob). This opens the 'Lower Gate', as it is known, to allow the Jing to pour in. However, to propel it upwards to the next station it is necessary to gently ease the tip of the coccyx outward with the assistance of both hip joints, while at the same time also twisting the waist in an anticlockwise motion (looking down).

5) Mingmen — Just like the Weilu, this point would have been curved at the commencement of the chain (convex lower back) but as the wave pours in through the gate, the spine at this location naturally moves forward, making the lower back concave. This action propels the Jing up to the next station along with the continued anticlockwise twisting motion (looking down).

6) Jaiji — This is an important major junction because from here the rising Jing can split two or three ways. In this case the Jing is being tracked along a single arm which involves a two-way split only — one over the shoulder and down the arm while the other traverses the Yu Chen point and over/through the head. (The three-way split is when the Jing flows directly down both arms and over/through the head simultaneously.) For the Jing to enter this gate and be propelled onward, the same method as described for the Mingmen must be employed.

7) Shoulder — At this stage the 'shoulder pump' kicks in after sensing the Jing has arrived. To activate the pump it is necessary to rotate the whole shoulder area forward and down, creating the image of a rolling wave.

8) Yuchen (Jade Pillow) — While the shoulder is being charged with Qi, a proportion of the original rising wave arrives at the Yuchen, which now plays a crucial role in directing and enhancing the flow down the respective limb. With the chin relaxed slightly forward and the Yuchen hollowed, the rising Qi gathers at the upper gate. The next phase, which is to propel it down the arm from the shoulder and over the crown (embracing the Baihui and Yintang cavities), involves simply lifting up the

head from the Baihui while focussing the eyes (and the Sky Eye) at a point in the distance. The transition from hollowed Yuchen to filled out Yuchen must be timed to fully correspond with the Qi travelling from the shoulder to burst outwards from the hand.

9) Elbow — As the shoulder rises so too does the elbow, but allow the shoulder to peak first. The elbow only rises (at the side of the body) to the height of the shoulder at rest, then naturally moves forward in a gradual downward spiral (anti-clockwise) while straightening out, ending up with the elbow tip pointing down. If applied correctly an obvious wave will be observed travelling down the arm to the wrist.

10) Wrist — When the Qi reaches this stage of its journey the Chinese say: 'One must settle the wrist for the Qi to burst forth into the fingers'. In other words, when the Qi wave hits the wrist, the arm is now fully extended (but not locked straight) with the wrist hanging limp (fingers pointing down). 'Settling the Wrist' (pointing the fingers up and lowering the wrist down) is like the crack at the end of a whip or a wave breaking and crashing on a beach; but note, do not leave the palm flat and facing forward; instead turn it in at 45° so that the Qi is released unimpeded.

Benefits of *Chan Su Chin*

1) Enhances the natural spiral patterns of the muscles, tendons, ligaments and joints.

2) Attunes the body to breathing the spiral rhythms of the universe.

3) The Silk Reeling drills and Tai Chi form postures are a natural therapy for the muscles, tendons, ligaments and joints generally.

4) Heightens the inner sense of Qi flow throughout all the Jinglo (meridians).

5) Lays the foundation for 'Total Body Breathing' (Grand Circulation).

6) Develops the potential for Qi transmission skill.

7) Increases martial proficiency.

Spirals

Nothing greater on earth is there to see
Than the spirals created by dynamic Qi.

– PTN

Step Five – Natural and Taoist Breathing

Now all the preceding steps come together when breathing is introduced to the combination. The breath (Qi) is the invisible link that unites and permeates all. In Tai Chi Chuan and general Taoist yogic practice, the two methods of breathing adopted are Natural Breathing and Taoist Breathing.

Natural Breathing

As its name implies, this is the regular pattern of breathing all surface dwelling creatures adopt and when it is functioning efficiently the Chinese call it 'Refreshing and Relaxing Breathing'. Natural breathing takes the form of the abdomen and chest (thorax) inflating (visibly expanding) on the in-breath and deflating (visibly contracting) on the out-breath.

If however this breathing function is abused it could rightly be re-titled 'Restrictive and Redundant Breathing'. For it to work efficiently, the torso sinews and spinal column joints must be kept flexible and soft, otherwise the muscles and bones will not expand and contract in support of the respiratory function.

Without such complementary conditions prevailing between breath and body, the diaphragm will be restricted and the lung tissue under-utilised. In respect of the diaphragm, poor posture curtails its free-flowing actions by congesting its vertical operating zone and thus limiting its desired range of movement.

The repercussions of this are that the lungs will only partially fill (inspiration) and partially empty (expiration), the former resulting in oxygen deficiency and the latter in carbon dioxide retention. The result is that the lower third of both lungs usually loses pliability and becomes stiff and leather-like due to lack of use. Natural breathing is the main breathing method in Tai Chi Chuan and if nurtured it becomes the best guarantee of a healthy performing body.

Taoist Breathing

A point of clarification is required at this juncture; the 'Natural Breathing' method just described is by definition 'Taoist' and should therefore not be pigeonholed as being outside of the Tao. When, however, the Chinese talk specifically of 'Taoist Breathing', they usually mean 'Reverse', or 'Condensing Breathing', (also known as 'Embryonic Breathing'), descriptive names that collectively combine to create 'Taoist Breathing'. It should be noted that Taoist Breathing is split into two camps: martial and health (physical/spiritual). The former is driven by the *Jing* (power) generated by the '*Heng* and *Ha*' method of breathing (Yang), while the latter concentrates on softening and refining the breath (Yin).

Reverse: As its name implies, this type of breathing involves reversing the normal processes of Natural Breathing. For example, on inhaling the abdomen should be gently drawn in and on exhaling relaxed to expand outwards. Although this is the reverse of 'Natural' it is by no means unnatural; to the contrary, it is in fact very natural and something all people do during their daily lives without realising. Reverse Breathing is unconsciously utilised during expressions of emotions, such as crying and laughing. When crying the abdomen is pulled in on the inward breath and when laughing the abdomen is pushed out on the outward breath.

Reverse respiratory action also appears during times of exertion. For example, when one attempts to extract a deep-rooted shrub great effort may be required on the pulling action. It is then, without the conscious mind's realising, that the abdomen is drawn in each time the shrub is tugged. The opposite, however, applies to the exertion of pushing a heavy car up a hill, where the body automatically slips into an exhalation on each push, coupled to an outward expansion of the abdomen.

Condensing: By reversing the breathing an unusual physiological change ensues involving the filtration of Qi and blood through the tissues and bones of the body. During inhalation Qi and blood are condensed into both the core of the abdomen (Real Dan Tien) and the bone marrow, a process that not only has physical but also metaphysical connotations.

The manifestation of the condensing principle in martial arts is seen when it is used to increase the power potential of punching, kicking, braking, piercing, pushing, pulling and grasping by up to 20%. For example, when pulling and grasping, the abdomen is condensed (drawn in) and when pushing or striking, the abdomen is naturally allowed to spring outwards after first condensing. In addition, it is used to create 'Body Armouring' (also known as Hard Qigong) where Qi and blood are packed (condensed) into the muscle fibres resulting in maximum efficiency, and thereby being able to withstand blows that might otherwise seriously damage an average person.

From a health perspective, condensing the Qi into the bone marrow cleanses the blood cells and strengthens the bones themselves, a point which has not gone unnoticed by the National Osteoporosis Society of Great Britain.

Breath of the Tao

From within stirs a power, a mystery of mysteries,

Carried on the faint breeze of inaudible breath.

– PTN

Step Six – Centre Movement

Here lies the ultimate step in the Earth-stage training process to illuminate the Middle Path. Composed of two parts, Step Six will unite all the preceding disciplines together through the unshackled, free-flowing energy/gravitational centres of the body, thus raising the physical form to a pinnacle of excellence and enabling ascendance of the Golden Steps. The two interlinked parts in order of practice are 'Central Equilibrium' and 'Centre Movement'.

Central Equilibrium

The Oxford English Dictionary describes *equilibrium* as 'A state of equal balance between two opposing forces or powers.' This, by definition, denotes that for this condition to exist there must be a *centre,* and only when equal balance becomes apparent within a body supported by the centre can there be equilibrium.

The focal point of this equilibrium is in fact the perfect middle of the Tai Chi T'u being exactly halfway along the 'S' curve that separates Yin from Yang. From here radiates outwards an awareness supported by the winds of Qi to all extremities of the body creating buoyancy and leaving the body free from clumsiness. Physically it materialises only when all three Dan tiens (*Real, Middle and Upper Dan tiens*) align and communicate to the extremities as follows:

- Right hand senses equilibrium with the left hand.
- Right/left hands sense equilibrium with the left/right feet respectively.
- Right foot senses equilibrium with the left foot.
- The Baihui senses equilibrium with the Huiyin.
- The Baihui senses equilibrium with The Yong chuans on the soles of both feet.

Central Equilibrium creates the symmetric body which operates in perfect balance, driven and directed by a central core of three Dan tiens. Therefore, if Central Equilibrium creates a universally aligned structure, something else is needed to make the structure move, and that something is 'Centre Movement'.

Centre Movement

When the body is in motion, all its actions according to Tai Chi Chuan teachings are to be coordinated through the waist. Whether moving up, down, forward, backward, left or right, the waist must be involved. To the uninitiated the waist collectively means hips and pelvic girdle, which visibly move when the body is in motion. Centre movement, however, is a non-visible (internal) aspect of physical motion that becomes the centre of gravity through which all external actions are linked or focussed.

The movements must therefore be channelled through and governed by an imaginary three-dimensional fist-size Tai Chi T'u, sitting in suspended animation at the location of the Real Dan Tien. This Yin and Yang ball should be supported by the Taoist breathing method and visualised as moving in the following manner:

Raising Upward (Inhalation) — This makes the body feel light and is especially developed in martial arts to make the kicking leg float, leap through the air, or assist the arms when lifting something vertically. (Note: The Huiyin is to be drawn in.)

Lowering Down (Exhalation) — The lowering of the centre to touch the Huiyin cavity in the pelvic floor has the opposite effect to that of raising the centre. This makes the Qi sink to the Yong chuans to make the feet and legs feel heavy, thus establishing a strong root. (Note: The Huiyin is to be relaxed down and outwards.)

Pulling Backwards (Inhalation) — The ball is drawn horizontally back to charge the spine (Ming men) with Jing or Qi. The spine is now charged with energy representing a bent bow (Weilu tilted slightly under) and Jing or Qi becomes the arrow released via the arms or legs (Weilu relaxed to hang down naturally). Martially, this is coordinated with a physical pull against an attacker, pulling him forwards onto his toes. From the health perspective, this will draw in Qi through the four limbs (Lougongs on palms and Yong chuans on feet) to nourish the torso and release negative Qi through the same.

A note of caution! The Middle Path gravity line moves from the Yong chuans to the heels when the centre is pulled back, making the body liable to fall backwards. If coupled with raising the centre it assists the body to leap backwards.

Pushing Forwards — When the ball is released from the spine it will naturally spring or recoil forwards to the Qihai bringing the Middle Path gravity line with it. This will, if unchecked, leave the body open to fall forwards as the gravity moves into the toes. If, however, this action is coupled with raising the centre it assists the body to gain uplift when leaping forwards.

Swivel Horizontally Left and Right — This turns the body to face the direction the centre is turning. For example, when turning left, (this is the reverse of the Yin and Yang cycle shown in Fig. 1) the body rotates anticlockwise with the left side visualised as a returning Yin force folding into the left Qua (the fold between the top of the thigh and the groin), which correspondingly drives the opposite forward moving Yang force round to the left (the same principle applies to a right turn). Swivelling the centre lies at the core of all turning movements and when united with the breath, directs Jing or Qi down and up individual arms or legs.

With practice all movements will become centralised and thus 'directed by the waist'. But this is not the complete picture, because although the Real Dan Tien is the most important cog of the machine in this science of perfect body motion, it is only when all three Dan tiens are harmonised that 'Grand Circulation' becomes a possibility, as will be seen in the next chapter.

Light at the Centre

From this day on a light will shine
To guide us through the dark,
As hope regains its impetus
Sustained as we embark.

– PTN

Chapter Nine
The Six Golden Steps of Tai Chi Chuan

A golden shroud, sweet speckled dew,
How fine this Earth's display,
Content I sit within your womb,
Safe — blessed by you this day.

– PTN

In Taoist teachings gold has a deeper meaning than just the precious metal much sought after by the material-minded world. It also represents the highest level of *Nei gong* (inner spiritual cultivation). The perfect being (one who has achieved enlightenment) according to classical Taoist imagery, stands betwixt Heaven (Gold) and Earth (Jade); this perfection is the result of uniting these two powers through the third power, the human form (*See Chapter 5*). Operating with a body that is free from blockages (internal stagnation), inner cultivation can progress once the physical development (Earth-stage) of the Jade Steps is complete.

Step One – The Three Treasures

The first consideration on the metaphysical journey is to establish the meaning of the Three Treasures (analogous to three fuels that, when successfully blended, produce the high octane fuel needed to power a sophisticated vehicle), which are Ching, Qi and Shen. All are forms of energy present in the human body; two of these (Qi and Shen) have been discussed in detail in earlier chapters. Here, however, we will consider the individual character, or Te, of each one.

Having identified the three, Step One will go on to advise on how to both conserve and nurture them before the mixing process begins.

The Three Defined:

Ching (Essence) — This form of energy operates at the lowest vibratory frequency and is described in the Taoist canons as the 'Coarse Essence' conveyed within the male and female sexual fluids. It also lies at the heart of 'that which gives matter tangible form and substance' and could therefore rightly be called 'the base Qi of creation'.

This implies that Ching is the catalyst which at the conception of a baby gives pre-birth Qi and Shen its form. At this stage all Three Treasures are at their purest untainted forms, which is why the Taoist sages talk of 'Returning to the Source' as being the desired destination for enlightenment seekers.

Qi (Vitality) — This, the next highest form of energy vibration, is more subtle than Ching and permeates the whole body to bring essential vitality for existence. It is derived from the parents' Original Essence, manifesting as pre-birth Qi, which then transforms at birth into postnatal Qi, the latter being sourced independently from air, food, drink and cosmic energies absorbed through the skin and cavities of the Jinglo (Meridians).

Shen (Earth Spirit) — This is the highest energy frequency in the human body and in its natural, uncultured form is classed as being 'Earth-bound'. In this state it is susceptible to degradation by complacency and ignorance, or conversely can be elevated to a higher frequency through the transmutation process of all Three Treasures described in Step Two. Additionally, in its Earthly state, it manifests as human will power, being the visible characteristics (Te) of an individual who, for example, 'shows spirit' or 'lacks spirit'.

Nurturing and Cultivation

Now that the three have been identified, they must be conserved and nurtured.

Ching — Resides in the kidneys and is negatively affected by excessive sexual ejaculations, an unbalanced lifestyle and emotional disturbance. As it is the root of the other two treasures, it must take precedence over the others in order of cultivation. An un-centred mind is where inordinate desire, greed and other negative emotions are conceived; therefore by centring the mind, negative emotions are suppressed, wisdom manifests and Ching conservation can begin.

The goal here, therefore, is to build up an abundance of Ching through moderation of sexual activity, coupled with the daily practice of Taoist exercise and meditation. By increasing awareness of the Huiyin cavity during the meditation process, Ching will accumulate around this cavity, which then acts as a catalyst for change and transformation as part of the process described in Step Two.

Qi — As with Ching, Qi must be conserved and not wasted. It must accumulate and be held in storage at the Real Dan Tien. This central reservoir of Qi forms the medium through which the transmutation of the Three Treasures can take place. Now that all six stages of the Jade Steps have been completed, conditions prevail for Qi to naturally accumulate (nothing forced).

Shen — This is the Ridgepole, the source of inner strength and human willpower, and the director of operations in the transformation process. Its residence is the heart, but when the blending process has been completed, it gravitates to a new home in the head behind the 'Sky Eye'. Neither Ching nor Qi control the Shen, although it can control them, but together, both Ching and Qi can raise Shen's energy frequency to an infinitely refined level.

In a modern free-thinking and sexually liberated society, total abstinence from the pleasure and joy of making love may not be the preferred option; fortunately, as the Tai Chi T'u represents good sense, moderation and balance, the Middle Path will still present itself.

The Light of Three Treasures

Those who venture from the dark

To relinquish selfish pleasures,

Find sanctity as they're guided to

The light born of Three Treasures.

— PTN

Step Two – Small Heavenly Circle

This is an internal yogic meditation process that intimately involves all Three Treasures; consequently, it is the vehicle of transformation that takes the traveller along the Middle Path journey to the centre. When purifying the Shen, it is important to know that visualisation directs, and breath fuels, this alchemic process which is also known as the 'Psychic Flow' and 'Microcosmic Orbit'. It involves the creation of a stronger, more refined natural flow of Qi around the circuit shown in fig. 7, which becomes the mechanism of transformation.

Small Heavenly Cycle Process

This circuit has a profound effect on the adept's physical and spiritual health and therefore should be afforded the utmost respect. The Chinese name for this mystic circuit is *Xiao Zhou Tien* and when broken down its true meaning becomes apparent:

- Xiao = Small
- Zhou = A Circle
- Tien = Heaven

Collectively this means '*A Small Circle Related to Nature and the Heavens*'.

Those who have penetrated its veiled secrets speak of amazing curative properties that have healed where traditional methods have failed. For the revitalised circuit to establish itself, a specific preparatory sequence needs to be followed. (This is a lengthy and involved process that will be described and illustrated in a future publication.) The preparatory sequence will gently dredge and change the exiting circuitry. (This will create a strongly flowing river, instead of a small trickling stream struggling to negotiate a course through life's imported debris and damage.)

Through regular practice, a smooth flow of refined energy (Golden Elixir) fills the circuit, bringing with it the beneficial side effects (improvements to the immune system, to breathing, posture, skin texture and colour and to internal organ efficiency). At this stage in the transmutation, a new home for the Purified Spirit is being constructed, located between the pituitary and pineal glands behind the Sky Eye.

The Fusion of the Three

This fusion of subtle energies
That bridges Heaven and Earth,
Creates a path that many walk
With no thoughts of death, but birth.
– PTN

Step Three – The Sky Eye

The higher-evolved Qi, now flowing through the Small Heavenly Circle, over a period of time evokes the gradual growth of the 'Shen Crystal', which is the new residence of the Purified Spirit. This inner eye is a psychic portal from which emerge many hitherto hidden powers (albeit as a trickle at first, for nature ensures the mind does not become mentally flooded with these superlative insights). The Sky Eye's opening to the outside world is located directly in front of the Shen Crystal and in the cavity known as the Yintang, through which Qi can be both drawn and released.

As the body is the vehicle for the Qi and Shen, it is important to remember that physical (external) cultivation must progress hand-in-hand with spiritual (internal) cultivation, for the light of the Purified Spirit to shine throughout. The Sky Eye stage of this dual cultivation lays the foundation for Step Six, because the Shen Crystal becomes both guide and director of operations for the revered Grand Circulation process. From here on in, an equal proportion of time will be spent both directing the Shen (with the Qi wrapped up in its wake) and simply observing (inwardly sensing) the inner alchemic processes.

Sky Eye Stimulation

The general training process for the Sky Eye is already established when the Small Heavenly Circle is in place; however, when the inner vision is focussed on the Yintang, the Yuchen and a newly formed Shen Crystal that sits between them, they collectively materialise inexplicable insights

Figure 9 – Sky Eye Meditation

that can be recognised as psychic. To make the Sky Eye breathe with increased potential entails setting up a daily regime of Taoist meditation practice. The methods described in SHC training must still be followed but in addition, in the midst of the Taoist breathing stage, Sky Eye development can be practised as follows. (*See fig. 9.*)

Having established 'Stillness' and 'Emptiness', raise both palms in front of the forehead, distanced about 30cm away, with the palms (Laogong points) angled in to connect with the energy of the Yintang. Reverse the breath and feel the Qi being drawn in through the Yintang Sky Eye and condensing at the imaginary position where the Shen Crystal sits. (This will tend to pull the hands in towards the Yintang — letting this happen helps one to feel its power.) To facilitate this, the head must be tilted back on the in-breath hollowing out the seat of the Yuchan (making it Yin receptive) and straightened up on the out-breath (making it Yang receptive).

As the head changes from Yin to Yang, release the imaginary arrow with the breath and at the same time turn the palms to face out. To sense the powerful flow of this 'Releasing Qi', the hands must be coordinated with the arrow's flight and move away (at the same height as the head) as if opening a pair of curtains that are in the way. This process should be repeated up to eight times; then close the Sky Eye as previously described and continue with the SHC meditation programme.

Note: Never proceed with Sky Eye training if you have a headache, temperature, or are prone to fluctuations in blood pressure.

Early Signals — Most people have psychic potential. This flows naturally in some, the psychics, while in others it is either on temporary vacation or permanently shutdown. By ascending the Golden Steps, those who have established abilities will notice the increased clarity permeating their 'gift'; and those who have never experienced its wonders will begin to receive early signals of its appearance.

Openness and a sensitivity to energy enables the adept to 'tune in' to 'Radio Paranormal', a non-commercial station that broadcasts from two locations: one, which operates on high-frequency, supernatural wavebands broadcast from between the layers of cosmic ether skirting the planet; the other broadcasts from the minds of fellow human beings, who in the main are unaware they are doing so. Attuning to the frequencies opens up a news network that surpasses anything CNN or the BBC can offer; for whilst they are able to analyse and report on current news items, they fail to present any account of events set to happen in, say… twelve months time.

Many people will have either experienced premonitions, or at least know what they are. From a Tai Chi Middle Path perspective, this not only encompasses the usual 'seeing things before they happen', but also the guiding light of inspiration that keeps the feet firmly planted on the right path. A good example is when a person inexplicably receives a communication (direct or indirect) that provides sufficient clarity to make sense of a situation that has been causing physical or emotional stagnation. Just how these transmissions appear can vary.

Dreams — As the Shen Crystal strengthens, personal frequencies graduate upwards to higher levels making it easier for spirit guides to communicate, especially during sleep.

In the main, dreams are simply re-runs of events witnessed during the day; there are, however, some exceptions that stand out from the crowd, carrying a message that may need interpretation. These are the special transmissions, imagery and messages within dreams that connect to higher guardians, or spirit guides who commune with human beings during sleep. At this stage of the Golden Step process, they are only able to break through the barrier that interfaces the physical and spiritual worlds when certain conditions prevail:

1) The brainwave pattern changes to a favourable frequency during sleep.

2) The mind is calm and free from distracting thoughts.

3) The spirit guide's frequency lowers sufficiently to 'cross the bridge'.

4) The Baihui (Heaven's Gate) is open (even partially).

Television and Radio — These two mediums usually play their part in transmitting the spirit's guidance when it is least expected. Here is an example: a major career opportunity has presented itself to someone in the form of a job offer that sounds too good to be true. The dilemma is whether to stay in the current job and patiently wait for the long-promised promotion, or to take the new opportunity and run the risk of failure in a bigger league.

On the day the deadline has arrived to make a decision, the bedside alarm goes off, heralding the start of just another day — or the beginning of a new career. Reaching over to switch the radio on, the person is greeted by a song with the refrain of 'it's time for change'.

Literature — In a library, bookshop or from their own bookshelf, someone picks up a book or magazine they feel drawn to and opens it at random, only to find the first words their eyes focus on conveys the message and guidance they require. The fact that they felt driven to pick up that book implies they were responding to instinct. And who was the motive force behind that impulse? Yes, their guide.

Conversations — Someone else may be sitting on a bus, train, aeroplane or anywhere humans congregate and suddenly they tune into words that rise above the background din, these words containing a unique message, which makes sense and provides the affirmation they have been searching for.

Having established a breathing and seeing Sky Eye through which the Shen journeys on the earthly plane, it is time to reach for even higher ground and look to the Heaven's Gate.

The Shen Crystal

The ancients grew a crystal
Which no barriers could constrain,
And through its light came visions
Rare, fed from a higher plane.

– PTN

Step Four – Heaven's Gate

At this stage the mysterious portal, known in English as the Heaven's Gate and in Chinese as the Baihui, makes its appearance, but, as with the Sky Eye, it will need some encouragement. When both of these powerful gates are open and cooperating, a whole range of psychic skills can be developed, which is why here, at Step Four, they must be discussed further.

Psychics and Mediums

The generally accepted view in the world of the paranormal is that mediums are psychic, but psychics are not mediums. The psychic tends to tune into Earth-bound frequencies using the extra-sensory perception of the Sky Eye to pick up from fellow humans (telepathy) or objects (psychometry), or on future human created events such as disasters, sporting achievements or terrorist acts, and naturally occurring events like earthquakes, hurricanes, and fires (premonition).

The medium although possessing these endowments can also operate on a higher psychic plane. The one subtle difference between the two is that the medium has developed the Heaven's Gate (*Baihui*) through which pours energy operating at a higher frequency than the energy of the Sky Eye.

This basic concept of frequencies is summarised in the following table:

Table 4: Pre-Cultivated Frequencies

Frequency	Density	Material
Low	High	Human
Medium	Medium	Coarse Ching
High	Low	Qi
Very High	Very Low	Shen

All material contained within the universe vibrates at variable specific frequencies which in turn dictate density. Typical examples at the lowest end of the earthly substances frequency scale would be the high-density materials titanium, diamond, platinum, lead and granite. While at the highest point of this scale appear gases (water vapour, air and smoke) and light particles (sun and moonlight) all with low density. Liquids, such as water, vibrate at a medium frequency, which uniquely creates medium density (halfway between a solid and a gas). This would suggest that water is a Middle Path material and it therefore comes as no surprise to see that the 'medium' of transformation from coarse to subtle and mortal to immortal is often depicted as water.

Table 5 reflects how both frequencies and density alter during the transformation process, the principle being that energy can shift its frequency to the benefit of the adept who is progressing along the Middle Path with dedication and natural unforced progress.

Table 5: Post Cultivated Frequencies

Frequency	Density	Material
Medium	Medium	Human
High	Low	Subtle Ching
Very High	Very Low	Real Qi
Highest	No Density	Pure Yang Shen

Aligning frequencies

To understand the world of psychics and mediums, we will analyse two well-known axioms: 'Like Attracts Like' and 'Opposites Attract'.

'Like Attracts Like' — An example of this is often seen on the school playground, where aggressive types see and sense a corresponding frequency in each other and naturally gravitate together. This, as mentioned in an earlier chapter, can be a destructive partnership because two or more people with the same Te (character) can at best perpetuate their ill doings (in the case of bullies) and at worst, sow the seeds of their own destruction (where the negativity spirals out of control). Therefore, in respect to mediums, it is important to understand that when opening up to the higher frequencies neither Yin nor Yang should dominate the mind of the receiver. Until the medium has found the Middle Ground (emotional balance), no attempt to commune should be made, otherwise the following two situations may materialise:

1) If a Yin person, lacking in confidence and discipline, and with low self-esteem and suppressed spirit, experiments with the Heaven's Gate, they could find themselves being manipulated by a similar negative spirit drawn to their weakness.

2) Conversely, if a Yang person, overbearing, aggressive and short tempered with low self-control and agitated spirit 'opens up', a similar spirit, happy to create havoc, may align to feed upon the resultant chaos.

'Opposites Attract' — When Yin attracts Yang, if the two show each other mutual respect and thus create harmony and balance, the 'Secret Garden' materialises. This is a wondrous place where both energies meet to commune, being the Middle Ground (Middle Path) of alignment and union. While the medium strides the Middle Path, elements from beyond the veil, be they Yin or Yang, cannot do them any harm, because in this hallowed place they have no power.

From this it is apparent that the catalyst for spiritual or earthly psychic communication is the Middle Path, which becomes both receiver and transmitter. For it to be a receiver, the path needs to be gently drawn into the Yin side. For it to be a transmitter it needs to move into the Yang side. During sleep the messages and images freely enter the subconsciousness, because Yin becomes the dominant force overnight. For any communication to enter the mind it has to be transmitted, which is by nature Yang and, as any true medium or psychic will confirm, their 'gift' strengthens and perpetuates only through regular meditation training.

The Search for Heaven

'I used to search for Heaven in
The night sky painted black,
But now I know someone like
Me is out there looking back.

If Heaven isn't out there, then
Where on Earth could it be?
But wait! Of course! At last
I know, Heaven is in me.

– PTN

Step Five – The Four Gates

With the 'Small Heavenly Cycle' well established and the transmutation process advanced, the next step is to clear the channels for 'Grand Circulation'. (*See Step 6.*) Up until this stage, a high proportion of time spent on internal cultivation has been while seated. However, to create true 'Grand Circulation', both standing and moving styles of Qigong, Taoist meditation and energy circulation drills (especially 'Silk Reeling' within the Tai Chi Chuan form) practised during the Earth-stage, have to be brought to the fore again.

Four Gates Breathing

The focal points of this method of cultivation are the 'Four Gates', located at the centre of each palm and sole of the foot respectively. These sites are where Qi naturally flows in and out, influenced and driven by normal respiration.

Four Gates Breathing is not to be confused with true 'Grand Circulation', although it does lie at its core, being the engine and medium through which the macrocosmic energies flow. Once again, it is necessary to quote an ancient Taoist doctrine which underlines the importance of this practice:

An ignorant man breathes from the chest.

A wise man breathes from the centre.

But enlightened is the man who breathes through the heels.

Golden Step 5 is concerned only with the 'enlightened man', the human beings who having successfully navigated their way out of ignorance and, having found wisdom, use it to illuminate the way to enlightenment (enlightenment in the sense of correct breathing method). Having established a respiratory pattern centred on the Real Dan Tien, the task now is to expand the breath outwards to also encompass the four limbs, thus creating 'Total Body Breathing'.

The Qi Body

A light now shines into the dark
Filling voids left by stagnation,
This sturdy frame replenished,
Forever crowned by restoration.

– PTN

Step Six – Grand Circulation: Transparency and Light

This final step is appropriately named 'Transparency and Light' because this is how the Taoist sages described the human body that has undergone spiritual metamorphosis. This is a transparent body, filled with shimmering white light lit by the glow of three Dan Tiens, fed by an ocean of 'Pure Cosmic Yang Shen' (the essence of the living universe). To the untrained eye, this awe-inspiring vision remains partially cloaked, although certain discernible physical characteristics do manifest. The hair thickens and takes on a natural sheen, the skin becomes smooth and peach-like and the eyes are sparkling and crystal clear in appearance.

Other noticeable changes include: accelerated growth-rate of hair and nails; a voice as clear as a bell; sharp and sensitive hearing; soft and long breathing; crisp and clear, in-focus eyesight, and a mind that finally relinquishes a common source of human weakness — summed up by one word that features in many Taoist canons: 'craving'. This radiance seen in these physical and metaphysical characteristics is the manifestation of Pure Yang Cosmic Shen through a body on the threshold of enlightenment, but to understand these phenomena, further analysis must be employed.

Physiology of Grand Circulation

The Jade Steps raise the body's cellular structure to a level through which refined spiritual vibrations can freely permeate. It is as if cloudy pond water has become crystal clear and free from impurities; the body has become translucent and is operating at its maximum potential.

When the Golden Steps do their duty, a lightness or buoyancy materialises creating for the adept an inner sense of transparency. The closest likeness to this joint physiological and ethereal state of being is witnessed when a miniature camera beams back the amazing images of a foetus from the depths of mother's womb. The unborn child's state of untainted translucency and innocence in the human form is the desired physical and spiritual condition for what the Sages call 'Returning to the Source'. This is what those who found the secret of the Middle Path aspired to, before leaving this mortal coil as immortalised Shen. The body is now an empty vessel free from tension and governed by a mind not constrained in any way by inordinate desires. This then is the transparency of Grand Circulation, a condition apparent when metaphysics and physics combine together, attuning with the rhythms of the Tao.

The Practice of Grand Circulation

It is time to go back to basics and look more closely at the true meaning of Tai Chi Chuan, in particular, the reasons why it also known as 'Cosmic Dance' and 'Moving Tao Meditation'.

Cosmic Dance — A more literal translation would be 'The physical manifestation of universal energy in the body achieved through the patterns of dance.' In other words, a rhythmic performance of perfect postures that attune with the energy of the cosmos.

Moving Tao Meditation — This is opposed to stationary (sitting or standing) Taoist meditation, which can mistakenly be assumed to be the preferred method chosen by the wise sages to achieve spiritual enlightenment. The reason for this assumption is that most images of Oriental enlightened beings, be they Buddhist, Taoist or of any other faith, are usually shown sitting in a cross-legged posture. Sages shown standing or depicted in meditative motion are few and far between, although to create inner conditions conducive for spiritual transformation, the sages of old insisted on the practice of Taoist exercise such as Tai Chi Chuan or Qigong.

To practise Grand Circulation, a pattern of regular practice will need imprinting into the body's biorhythms and Qi-flow cycles, so that it almost becomes as necessary as breathing. Twice a day, morning and evening, will stimulate the correct balance between Yin and Yang Qi, bearing in mind a morning workout must differ in approach from that practised in the evening.

Morning Programme

Because this is the Yang part of the day, the workout must be geared to clean out the stagnant Yin Qi which has accumulated overnight (that feeling of sluggishness that is present upon waking) and replace it with morning-fresh Yang Qi. A typical morning session would therefore be thus:

1) Whenever possible train outside just as dawn is breaking and face the rising sun.

2) Select Qigong exercises that shake the joints and release the muscles and tendons.

3) Select Qigong exercises that flex the Jade Pillar (spine) and stimulate cardiovascular and respiratory functions.

4) Stand with feet shoulder-width apart and hands over the Qihai and kick-start the Microcosmic Orbit.

5) Immediately flow into Four Gates Breathing to clear the channels of the limbs.

6) With the basic Macro-Cosmic Orbit established, proceed to perform the Tai Chi Form.

Evening Programme

Because it is the Yin part of the day and the body and mind are winding down, the session must be structured to release the remnants of active Yang Qi carried over from the day and therefore the focus must be on calming and centring.

1) Still train outside if possible and face the east from where the Yin energies are emerging. If training inside, open the window for fresh air and face east.

2) As 2 in the morning programme, but gentler in approach to release Yang Qi.

3) As 3 in the morning programme, but again gentler.

4) As 4, 5, and 6 in the morning programme, but become more sensitive to allow Tai Chi Sung to manifest.

5) Having experienced Sung, find a comfortable place to sit in peace and quiet and finish the session with the hands over the Qihai, breathing naturally (not reverse) to centre and find stillness.

TAI CHI SUNG

In the context of Taoist inner alchemy, this translates to mean 'No Limits', which is how one would describe the euphoric sensations of limitless power that surge throughout the body when Sung makes its appearance. The following account of an adept's first encounter with Sung gives a good insight to this phenomenon:

Late one evening I prepared my mind and body in the usual way and began to perform Tai Chi form with no expectations. Within a couple of minutes a deepening sense of relaxation enveloped me, assisted by the completely silent atmosphere of the room in which I had chosen to practise. This was followed by what I can only describe as a feeling of letting go, as if my body and mind were free from all emotional or physical distractions. On this occasion the gradual descent into a calm mind and relaxed, flowing body unexpectedly moved into a new dimension as a deeper state of inner emptiness unfolded, that initially left me feeling a little apprehensive.

Instead of operating at the usual interface between the spirit and the physical (a point of consciousness in which is sensed the omnipresent 'now'), I seemed to have sunk, or, should I say, been elevated, to a whole new level of sensitivity, as if I had retreated deeper in my physical self to a place of infinite calm, although still retaining a sense of the 'now', albeit removed to arm's length. Everything took on a slow motion appearance, as if time itself were 'taking it easy', but the most surprising thing was how my body was responding in an almost disjointed way to my willing it to move.

This experience transformed into an enjoyable and emotionally enlightening ride within my own body, I had become the passenger inside my human form, an ethereal Qi body, totally buoyant, free from the grip of gravity, which was directing all the sophisticated Tai Chi Chuan postures with a mere thought. I likened it to being sat back in a comfy chair witnessing the whole thing from deep within the core of my existence but able to tap into a force of unimaginable potency. When I finally came to the end of the form at the cessation of all physical movements, it took a split second to re-cross the threshold into consciousness and regain full control of myself.

To summarise *Sung*, it is when both spiritual and physical bodies have mutually opened up a new and more refined level of vibration (frequency) allowing the subconscious mind (Shen) to conduct proceedings ('applying the will, not force'). This leaves the conscious mind to experience a deeper sense of comfort, relaxation and awareness from the safety of the Middle Path ('Serenity in Activity').

Purified Stillness

This simple and yet vitally important aspect of inner cultivation is grossly misunderstood and underestimated. In terms of being 'still', it is quite clear to those at this stage of the journey that there are varying forms of stillness; from just being silent and not moving a muscle to the sublime stillness enveloping the Middle Path in atmospheric bliss. To find sublime stillness it is advisable to commence with the former by standing or sitting in silent, motionless (except for the soft waves of breathing flowing through the torso) stillness.

With regular practice, a sense of inner peace emerges enveloping the senses like a misty cloud (Purified Stillness), and while one lingers in this serene place, the 'Golden Elixir' gives birth to the 'Spirit Child' in the womb of the Shen Crystal. (*See Chapter 10.*)

The stillness of Grand Circulation is designed to create a void in which Shen consolidates in a body totally transparent (not just the torso). This refined spiritual body is then transmuted into 'Pure Cosmic Yang Shen' by blending it with externally sourced Cosmic Shen Qi. Until the body has ascended to the level of transparency, this internal yogic process will be unachievable.

Shen Defined

As explained earlier, Shen is the Chinese word for 'Spirit' and as the Golden Steps and everything that lies beyond are inextricably linked to these latter phases of training, it is essential to become intimately acquainted with Shen.

Here is what is generally regarded as the western interpretation of the word *spirit*:

1) The general characteristic of a living being (also known as Te).
2) The willpower of an individual.

3) The sense of self.

4) One's enthusiasm and energy for life.

5) One's attitude or state of mind.

6) An emotional attitude attached to a group (football team, work departments etc).

7) The influential and inspirational force of a deity or person/s.

8) The prevailing mood, for example, of a country prior to the outbreak of war.

9) The ethereal body (non-physical) of an individual, also called the soul.

10) The earthly manifestation of a person's energy body after death.

11) The description of the soul as it crosses over between Heaven and Earth.

In Taoist sciences, however, they look a little deeper when defining the true essence of the word. According to the sages of old, the Shen is the 'lord of the body' and would, if unladen of the body's emotional and physical baggage, naturally evolve in its energy frequency.

The Shen manifests at the moment of conception in the mother's womb and at this moment its state can be described as pure. However, as mentioned earlier, it will only remain so providing it is not loaded down with 'baggage'. There is also another course of action beyond that of freeing the Shen: it is that of spiritual enlightenment, where the Shen is cultivated to its highest state of existence/non-existence. To the enlightenment seeker, clearing away the 'baggage' is only the first half of the journey; the second half is the process of refinement which equates to adopting the Jade and Golden routes of study and practice respectively.

The process of cultivating Grand Circulation will also free the Shen to do its functional work, which according to Lao-tzu is that of director of operations behind all essential bodily functions such as cardiovascular, respiratory, endocrine, emotional, Qi-circulatory, reproduction and the instinctive digestive (Yang) and expulsive (Yin) needs. With such an important role in the health and wellbeing of the body, wise are the adepts who seek out and nurtures their True Nature or Shen.

In contrast to a Shen evolving through cultivation is a Shen polluted by ignorance. Within Taoism there also is a belief that if through ignorance the Shen becomes shackled and cloaked in layers of negativity, as when someone abuses their body habitually and is uncentred both physically and emotionally, then if that person dies prematurely so too does the Shen.

True cultivation of the Shen unleashes the 'Iron Guardian', as it is known in Taoist circles; this ensures the Shen lives on at the end of the physical body's life: a favourable condition the Chinese call 'dying healthy'.

At the 'Gateway to Marvels', it is best to adopt a cautious attitude when opening up the senses while in meditation. If there remain the embers of human frailty in the form of negative thoughts, especially at this level of refined frequency, these may attract negative spirits who may only be too pleased to steer the adept off the Middle Path and onto rough, uncharted and dangerous ground.

'The human mind is like iron but a cultivated mind is like gold'

— Taoist Precept

It is clear this precept offers a warning to those who attempt to walk the higher ground. The reference to iron signifies that human thoughts tend to be impure, which is seen as the corrosive effects of rusting. The cultivated Tao mind is the desired goal, and is therefore described as gold to represent the purest of thoughts.

The Golden Elixir

If ordered to the surface to
Be at our beck and call,
It recoils and spirals deeper
Offering no response at all.

The only way to draw it forth
This tender golden dove,
Is bind its beak with silken
Thread and lead it from above.

— PTN

Chapter Ten
Beyond Enlightenment

I think I've finally got here,
This must be Heaven's door.
But wait! Isn't that? No it can't be!
It's true! I've seen this place before!

– PTN

How do the living describe what lies beyond the luminescent veil? The majority will have to wait until life runs its natural course before encountering the truth. However, some do acquire a foresight, either by near-death experience, or through spiritual cultivation. This chapter will attempt to describe what the Taoist Immortals encountered when they became bathed in the celestial light of the heavens.

This journey beyond the veil of normal human consciousness will take the form of an analysis of the true Taoist journey through the four phases of existence: birth, life, death and afterlife. With the accompaniment of the great sages, a silken thread of wisdom centrally linking all phases (Middle Path) will be spun. In addition, the analysis of the various stops along the way will shed light onto the many cryptic clues that tantalisingly tease as to what exists beyond enlightenment.

The journey begins at birth but it is not the beginning of the journey for the Shen for, as will become clear, the Shen of the Taoist adept has no beginning and no end. According to Taoist belief, at the very moment of conception in the mother's womb a mysterious gateway opens through which appears the spirit-body of the newly forming foetus. With this gateway at its core, the embryo now takes shape around it and, from this, it can be seen that the Shen lies at the core of the human being.

Without the existence of this embryonic spirit the physical body would not develop into a fully formed baby. This principle also applies to what happens at the time of death, when the spirit leaves the physical body, which instantly begins to degenerate and ceases to exist.

Cultivated Enlightenment

What is enlightenment? Is it simply the acquisition of knowledge previously unknown to the individual? This is the normal appreciation of its meaning, when considering it in a non-spiritual sense. However, when viewed from a purely spiritual perspective, it takes on a new definition. Within a human lifetime, all, except those who have been recalled back to the source by means of murder, accident, illness or self-extinguishment, are given the opportunity to benefit themselves and others.

For their own benefit, they could aspire to raising their energy frequency so that they are able to commune with and work with their spirit companions and guides, who are tasked by the Tao to ensure transformation and change continue on this planet. For the benefit of others, they could shine a ray of hope into the dark zones where breed hatred and despair. Though not all aspire to the state of immortality, they have walked at least some of the way along the jewel-encrusted highway of the Middle Path, and grateful are those who have bathed in their light during this time. Some take up the challenge and make credible progress along the ascending path and, out of the countless thousands who contribute to this honourable task, only a handful reach the summit. Those who surpass themselves with commitment, dedication and much personal sacrifice become the chosen few who are exposed to the truth of enlightenment.

For they are returning home, 'light of foot', unhindered by life's traumas, in touch with their soul and all its memories, complete in who they were, are and will be. If they, the chosen ones, are relieved from the cycle of reincarnation it makes sense to assume they will join the elite… the guardian angels.

FIGURE 10 —
'MIDDLE PATH GRAPH OF LIFE, DEATH AND REBIRTH'.

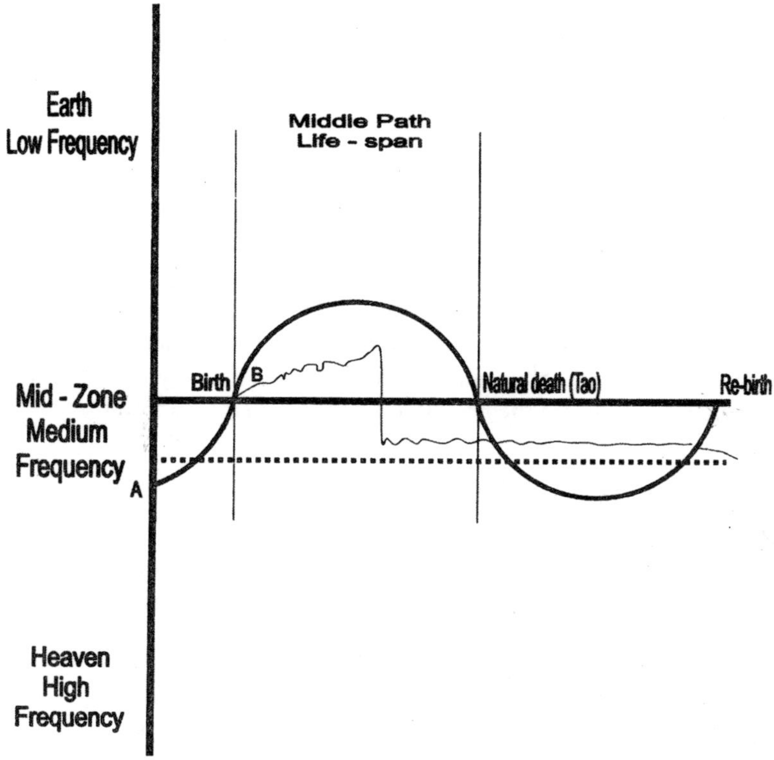

In figure 10 person 'A' enters life with a smooth transition from the source and is clearly seen to align with the pulse of the Tao, represented by a smooth, unwavering and long 'life-line' (Middle Path). While 'B', on the other hand, enters the world with the same potential and expectations but soon succumbs to earthly weaknesses and walks outside the warmth of the Middle Path, indicated by the erratic route followed. By not embracing the Tao, soon 'B's' forces are turned inwards gradually eroding 'B's' life force which finally and suddenly implodes under the self-imposed pressure and drops out of life into the 'Mid-Zone' with a splash. It is here where baggage-laden spirits are processed, where the infinite powers recalibrate these misguided souls. The time taken to refine a spirit is seen when comparison is made between the time 'A' spends in the spirit world to that of 'B', who clearly is retained for a much greater period. 'A' is reborn to continue the 'mission' far more quickly than 'B', who may take two lifetimes or more before returning to Heaven (on Earth).

Along the lower slopes of life, expectant eyes
Of innocence gaze out in wonder, then with
The passing of time, fate deals its fickle hand.

– PTN

There can be nothing in the human life cycle that compares to the innocence of a baby's eyes, eyes that reflect a resplendent soul. This glowing purity of innocence (Shen) in a newly born child is very apparent to the proud parents who for the first time look into their baby's eyes.

Children and the Spirit World

During the first few years of life some children encounter visions of the world of spirits. Usually they show no fear in these encounters except when one is seen in a place where the child knows only its parents visit, such as the child's bedroom. The mind of the child can still be compared to gold and, as mentioned earlier, gold nullifies the power of unwanted entities, so the child does not feel threatened. It is often mentioned in spiritualistic circles that spirits are drawn to the children; seen through the eyes of the troubled spirits a child would appear as pure white radiant light that could shed its warmth on their darkness.

The Mysterious Gate

When viewing the Tai Chi T'u from a spiritual perspective (White Yang = Life, Solid, Real, Physical World and Black Yin = Ethereal, Intangible, Non-physical, Spirit World) the symbol's representation of the Mysterious Gate is shown as the black dot of Yin in the white head of Yang, being the portal through which the spirit-body travels from the physical to the non-physical universe.

To burst into life and fall naturally
Into decline, yes, this is life's way.

– Taoist Precept

This precept offers a warning about how the energies of the white and black dots configure within the symbol as a whole. For example, when only focussing the eyes on the Yin portion, it should be viewed as though one were looking from the spiritual world through the White Gate at the physical opposite. To cross over through the gate will require a great deal of effort (*just as great energy needs to be expended by humans to conceive and, especially, to give birth to new life*).

At the other end of the spectrum, looking solely at the White Yang portion as representing physical life and peering through the Black Gate into the spirit world, the opposite prevails. Hence when the time is right, the Black Gate representing death positively sucks the poor soul through without any effort required to assist the process.

The Mysterious Gateway it is a gate which swings both ways, one way to let the purified spirit cross over into life and the other to allow it to return back to the source (irrespective of its condition). The Mysterious Gateway is not only regarded by Taoists as the portal through which life emerges and finally returns, it also has a deeply spiritual meaning and in this context is a much sought after gem. And yet in the general wheel of life it somehow locates the person when the time is right, be it birth or death. For those who walk the Middle Path and have entered through this secret portal also describe it as 'the Golden Palace' or 'the Realm of Tai Chi'. This therefore is a place of much reverence and the Grand Ultimate (Tai Chi) goal of immortality seekers. Based on this dual view of the Mysterious Gateway it is easy to be drawn into believing the Gate itself manifests into differing levels of spiritual existence subject to the extent the Shen has been cultivated or degraded.

The critical questions to ask at this juncture are:

1) Where is the Mysterious Gate?

2) How is it opened?

In respect of where it is found, statements made by the many revered Taoist and Confucian scholars serve only to leave the adept more confused than before the question was asked.

According to one of my teachers, Master Yang Jwing-Ming, the gateway is accessed through the Real Dan Tien Gate but in order to enter the gate the other key psychic centres (*see fig. 7*) must also be simultaneously opened. If the gate is unable to materialise at one of the psychic centres, then Grand Circulation cannot be achieved. This explains why Grand Circulation is the highest pinnacle of spiritual achievement. It is safe therefore to assume the Tao, though not being accessed in these locations, will be found collectively *through* them, acting like a circle of crystals, each breathing life into a shimmering 'star gate' or window.

The Spirit Child

It is traditional for Taoists to contemplate on how all things are equal and how a child-like spirit is no different from the simplicity and beauty of a butterfly.

The Great Journey

Visualise dozens of caterpillars that start their lives at the foot of a giant oak tree in a vast forest, which spreads from horizon to horizon. The Tao in its infinite wisdom has genetically encoded the caterpillars with one irrepressible instinct, to climb to the uppermost branches of the great green canopy, which in the context of the Tao is their heavenly goal. Something in their tiny, limited minds tells them 'time is of the essence', for somehow they know they must reach their final destination before the shadow of expiration is cast upon them. Other than a need to eat and take on board fuel for the journey, their minds are free from distracting thoughts, giving clarity to their focus.

The great journey is hard, full of danger as many are 'picked off' by predators along the way — the most hazardous part being the lower half of the tree, where predatory creatures are in abundance, particularly attracted by the young Qi-filled caterpillars. Yet, a chosen few defy the odds and through dogged determination finally reach journey's end to witness the marvellous sight now materialising before them. A world now appears which before they had not even known to exist; to them the darkness and uncertainty of life's expectations under the forest canopy was all they could perceive as being their world. Commendably, they have fulfilled the directive of the Tao, but are unable to behold this wonder that now arrays itself before them. They feel its warmth and bathe in its brilliance, but still cannot see what is to them 'Caterpillar Heaven'.

For the final few caterpillars, this then is the end of their earth-stage existence. The Tao however, in gratitude for their unselfish Herculean effort rewards them not with death, but with life, reborn as higher evolved creatures that can explore this new and exciting world, free from earthly bonds. And so with the natural conclusion of the caterpillar's lifespan, there emerges beautiful spirit-like butterflies imbued with child-like awe at the boundless universe lying at their feet.

The Spirit Child should not be mistaken for another entity beyond the spirit-body; both are in fact one and the same. The term *Spirit Child* is used by some sages to mean the evolution and transmutation of the Shen as it emerges from a human body in unshackled child-like exuberance.

The Tao is the father and mother,
And their cultured Qi the precious child.

– Taoist Precept

If the father and mother are Yang and Yin respectively (Tai Chi), then the Precious Child is the result of this perfect union. This, in terms of spiritual evolution, confirms it is only at the centre (between the two opposites) that a Spirit Child can emerge; this once again underlines the importance of establishing a personal Middle Path.

So far, the discussion has evolved around the afterlife period of the Spirit Child, but there is another facet to consider, the pre-death period when the cultivated Shen conceives the embryo Spirit Child. This is a period of time when this embryonic vehicle allows the conscious mind to transcend the boundaries of the physical world and for the first time take a long hard look (not just glimpses and insights) at the Yin world through the Mysterious Gate.

Near Death Experience

Those who have had near death experiences are commonly known in the medical circles as temporary flat-liners, people who are escorted to the 'light' during those few short minutes that span between heart seizure and rectification, or restart. Most talk of feeling totally at peace and free from pain, as they are drawn closer to its source. Others say they were reunited with loved ones who had already crossed over. And then there are those who witness events unfolding around their prostrated bodies. They talk of having hovered like early morning mist on still air, watching the frantic attempts by the hospital staff or roadside paramedics to resuscitate them. Common to all these experiences, however, is the soft reassuring voice of their spirit guides, who, much to their surprise, announce, 'It's not your time to join us. You still have things to do.'

The recipients of this amazing experience speak of it being 'life changing' or 'a major turning point in my life'. Many years and experiences later, it is obvious to them why they were spared, as they reflect on all the positive things that would not otherwise have materialised if they had been 'welcomed into the light' at the time.

Spirit Memory

For the spirit to reach its full potential, the 'Guardians of the Universe' (as some Taoist canons call them) may deem it necessary that it passes through more than one lifetime. Some say the soul may need to be given the opportunity to redeem itself after mistakes and indiscretions carried over from a previous existence.

In Taoist thinking the soul does have a memory that generally is inaccessible to burdened human consciousness. However, when the enlightenment seeker draws near to the Middle Path, insights of previous lives can filter through, and as the adept reaches enlightenment the whole of the soul memory becomes available, making sense of the myriad of experiences in both current and past lives.

APPENDIX

Notes and Sources

GENERAL

1. Throughout the book quotations appended with PTN are all created by the author.

2. All other quotations unless otherwise indicated are of folklore origin.

CHAPTER ONE

1. Yang Jwing-Ming, *Tai Chi Secrets of the Yang Style* (Boston: YMAA Publication Center, 2001)

2. Lin Yutang — *The Importance of Living* (London: William Heinemann, 1941)

CHAPTER FIVE

3. Lin Yutang — *The Importance of Living* (London: William Heinemann, 1941)

CHAPTER SIX

4. Fung Yu-Lan — *'A Short History of Chinese Philosophy'.* (New York: Free, 1976)

List of Illustrations

Bibliography

Dang Li, *Chinese Functional Food*, (Beijing: New World Press, 1999).

Fung Yu-Lan, *A Short History of Chinese Philosophy*, (New York: The Free Press, 1976).

Harvey, Peter, *An Introduction to Buddhism* (Cambridge: Cambridge University Press, 1990).

Lin Yutang, *The Importance of Living* (London: William Heinemann Limited, 1941).

Yang Jwing Ming, *The Root of Chinese Chi Kung* (Boston:YMAA Publication Center, 1989).

Yang Jwing Ming, *Tai Chi Secrets of the Yang Style* (Boston:YMAA Publication Center, 2001).